STAIR SAINTY MATTHIESEN

D1501303

In association with MATTHIESEN, 7–8 Mason's Yard, Duke Street, St.James's, London SW1

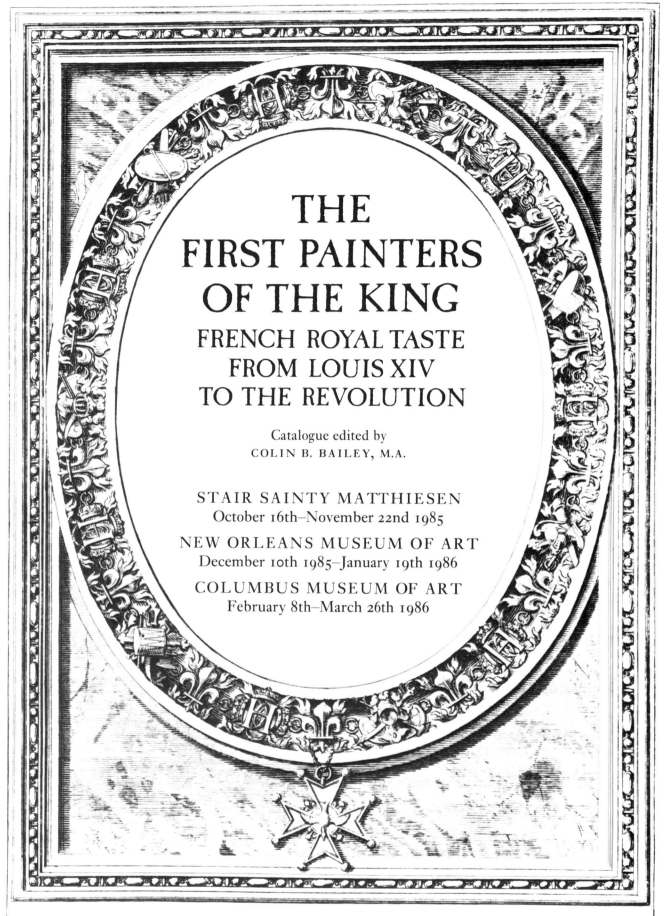

THE FIRST PAINTERS OF THE KING

FRENCH ROYAL TASTE
FROM LOUIS XIV
TO THE REVOLUTION

Catalogue edited by
COLIN B. BAILEY, M.A.

STAIR SAINTY MATTHIESEN
October 16th–November 22nd 1985

NEW ORLEANS MUSEUM OF ART
December 10th 1985–January 19th 1986

COLUMBUS MUSEUM OF ART
February 8th–March 26th 1986

STAIR SAINTY MATTHIESEN
141 East 69th Street, New York, New York 10021
M.D.CCCC.LXXXV

Catalogue designed by Graham Johnson
Printed in England by Lund Humphries, London & Bradford

Contents

This exhibition is held under the gracious patronage of His Royal Highness Monseigneur Alfonso of Bourbon, Duke of Anjou and Cadiz, Head of the Royal House of Bourbon.

Acknowledgements

This exhibition would not have been possible without the considerable contribution of a number of people. I am particularly grateful to Colin Bailey who has been engaged in researching and producing the catalogue entries for each work for the past year and has always been ready with useful advice, even when telephoned in Paris in the middle of the night. The collation of the inventory of paintings by the ten First Painters in US public collections is the work of Alan Wintermute who contacted over 350 museums and, in addition to dealing with the complex bureaucracies of museums' registrars' departments, has had to evaluate and research nearly 180 paintings.

I am most grateful for the interesting and informative essays from Professors Philip Conisbee, of the University of Leicester, Professor Jean-Luc Bordeaux of California State University, Northridge, and Professor Thomas Gaehtgens of the Frei University, Berlin. Both M. Pierre Rosenberg, Conservateur-en-Chef of the Department of Paintings of the Louvre, and Alastair Laing have always been ready with advice and we would also like to acknowledge the assistance of M. Thierry Le François and Marie-Catherine Sahut of the Department of Paintings of the Louvre and Dr Andrew Ciechanowiecki of the Heim Gallery, London, Mr Richard Herner of Colnaghi, London, and Mr Joseph Baillio of Wildenstein and Company, New York.

This exhibition would not have been possible without the generous co-operation of the lenders, Mr David Brooke and the Trustees of the Sterling and Francine Clark Art Institute, Williamstown, Massachusetts; Mr M. Kirby Talley, Jr, and the Trustees of the Allen Memorial Art Museum, Oberlin College, Ohio; Mr John Bullard and the Trustees of the New Orleans Museum of Art; the Marquis de Lastic; and those lenders who wish to remain anonymous. I would like to thank John Bullard and Ed Caraco of the New Orleans Museum of Art and Budd Harris Bishop and Steven Rosen of the Columbus Museum of Art for their assistance in organising the second and third venues for the exhibition.

Special thanks are due to Ali Elai of Camerarts who photographed nearly all the paintings in the exhibition, Frank Zuccari for his conservation work and Patrick Matthiesen and John Lishawa of Matthiesen Fine Art, London. I am also grateful for the help of Simon Parkes, Alain Goldrach, Claude Rigosi and J. P. Pigault, all paintings conservators, Edmond Torn and Matthew Rutenberg for their assistance and researches, and Irwin Rosen of Hudson Shipping. My secretary, Janet L. Friedman, has put up with mountains of extra work and receives my greatest thanks; and, my wife, Cynthia, in addition to helping with research, has been most tolerant during the inevitable crises in the organisation of this exhibition.

Guy Stair Sainty

The Royal House of France

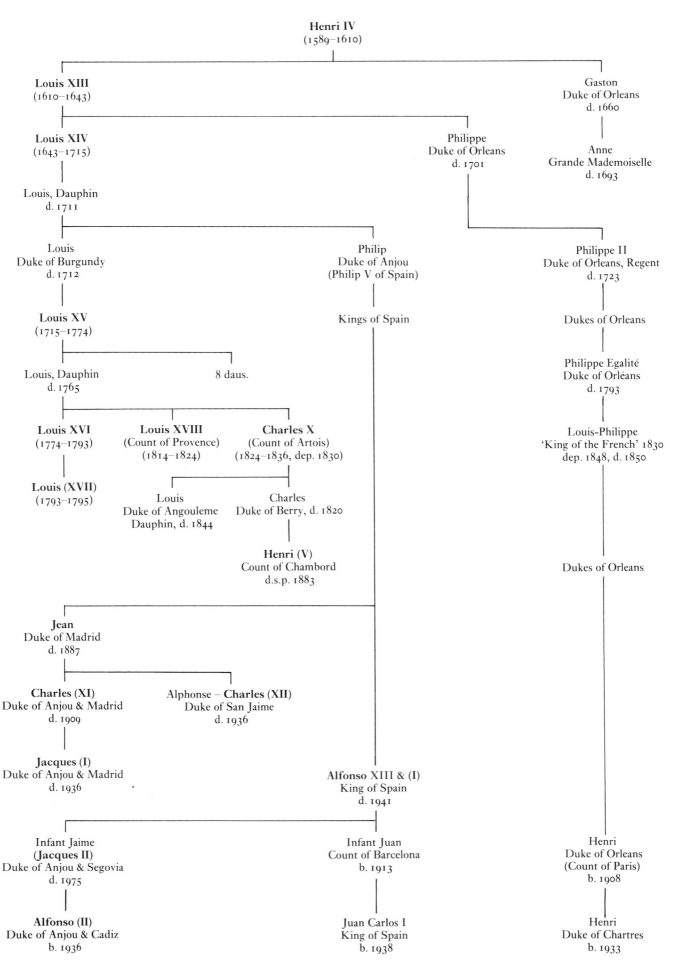

Henri IV
(1589–1610)

Louis XIII
(1610–1643)

Gaston
Duke of Orleans
d. 1660

Louis XIV
(1643–1715)

Philippe
Duke of Orleans
d. 1701

Anne
Grande Mademoiselle
d. 1693

Louis, Dauphin
d. 1711

Louis
Duke of Burgundy
d. 1712

Philip
Duke of Anjou
(Philip V of Spain)

Philippe II
Duke of Orleans, Regent
d. 1723

Louis XV
(1715–1774)

Kings of Spain

Dukes of Orleans

Louis, Dauphin
d. 1765

8 daus.

Philippe Egalité
Duke of Orléans
d. 1793

Louis XVI
(1774–1793)

Louis XVIII
(Count of Provence)
(1814–1824)

Charles X
(Count of Artois)
(1824–1836, dep. 1830)

Louis-Philippe
'King of the French' 1830
dep. 1848, d. 1850

Louis (XVII)
(1793–1795)

Louis
Duke of Angouleme
Dauphin, d. 1844

Charles
Duke of Berry, d. 1820

Henri (V)
Count of Chambord
d.s.p. 1883

Dukes of Orleans

Jean
Duke of Madrid
d. 1887

Charles (XI)
Duke of Anjou & Madrid
d. 1909

Alphonse – Charles (XII)
Duke of San Jaime
d. 1936

Jacques (I)
Duke of Anjou & Madrid
d. 1936

Alfonso XIII & (I)
King of Spain
d. 1941

Infant Jaime
(Jacques II)
Duke of Anjou & Segovia
d. 1975

Infant Juan
Count of Barcelona
b. 1913

Henri
Duke of Orleans
(Count of Paris)
b. 1908

Alfonso (II)
Duke of Anjou & Cadiz
b. 1936

Juan Carlos I
King of Spain
b. 1938

Henri
Duke of Chartres
b. 1933

INTRODUCTION

The First Painters of the King

by Guy Stair Sainty

When isolated from their contemporaries, there appears to be little connection between the grand scenes of history by Le Brun and the decorative paintings of Boucher, the extravagance of Le Moyne and neo-classicism of Vien. Their selection as First Painter of the King was an indication of both the respect with which they were regarded and the changing, but sometimes outdated, tastes of the Kings of France and their Court. The period from the official appointment of Le Brun in 1664 to the disappearance of the title of First Painter in 1792 coincides with the most glorious era in the history of the French Monarchy, and it was the principal duty of the First Painters to reflect that glory in their art. The title was inevitably limited to history painters, and this exhibition only includes historical, religious or mythological subjects.

The most important patrons of history painters,[1] whose repertory included both sacred and profane subjects, were the Crown and Church. Sponsorship of the visual and plastic arts was carefully controlled on the Crown's behalf by the Superintendent, later Director-General, of the King's Buildings, in collaboration with the members of the Royal Academy of Painting and Sculpture. These important officers were appointed by the King and could directly influence the development of official taste, particularly in the encouragement of history painting. Church patronage was also extensive during the late seventeenth and eighteenth centuries and along with the Crown offered a constant source of commissions for history painters of the Academy. However, there was no central control of patronage, which depended primarily on the taste, interest and wealth of the Prelate or Order commissioning the work. Several of the First Painters, notably Mignard, Antoine Coypel, Boullongne and Pierre, made their early reputations as painters of religious subjects. These pictures were seen by a large audience and satisfied the often deeply held religious beliefs of the painters themselves, although the artists were paid much less for them than for secular subjects.

The decision to give formal status, through a royal *brevet*, to the title of First Painter was part of Colbert's plan to centralize control of the arts. Whether the title conferred real power or was intended to be largely honorific is not immediately apparent. Reference to the royal letters patent granting the appointment shows that these only outlined the responsibilities in the broadest terms. Their form was similar in each case, not specifying any duties, although they conferred on the holder all the 'honors, authorities, powers, pre-eminences, prerogatives, privileges, franchises and liberties that pertain to the office'.[2] Neither Van Loo nor Boucher chose to exercise the administrative functions of their charge, while in contrast Le Brun, C. Coypel and Pierre were deeply involved in their official roles. Although not specifically stated, the appointment was in practice for life. Le Brun's power, however, only lasted while he had the continuing support of his immediate superior, the Superintendent.

The position of First Painter should not be confused with that of the Director of the Royal Academy.[3] The latter was elected to his office, did not necessarily hold the post for life and his authority was limited to Academy affairs. All the First Painters, with the exception of Le Brun,[4] already held or were elected to the Directorship of the Academy, but Van Loo and Boucher both resigned the post to others, while many of the Directors were never appointed First Painter. The selection of each holder was not only recognition of his artistic achievements but also of his administrative ability. In the cases of C. Coypel and Pierre, the latter may have weighed more heavily in their choice. Furthermore, with the notable exception of Le Brun and Le Moyne, the appointment did not acknowledge the current position of the artist but was granted in recognition of past artistic achievements – Boucher was aged 62 on his appointment, Boullongne 71, Vien 73 and Mignard 78 and were well past their prime. The First Painters were supposed to be viewed as an example both to their peers and succeeding generations of painters, successfully embodying the academic ideal. Hence Bernard Lepicié's selection of tributes to the earlier First Painters in his 'Vie des Premiers Peintres' published in 1752.

Although Le Brun was the first artist appointed officially to the post, the title had been used earlier by Vouet, apparently with Royal assent, as acknowledgement of his pre-eminence in French artistic life. It was not until nine years after Vouet's death that Le Brun was described unofficially as First Painter of the King, in the baptismal certificate of a friend's child in November 1658. Two years later, in an official document of June 16th 1660 he was referred to as *first painter of the King and of his royal Academy*. Ennobled in December 1662 and granted the title of *Ecuyer* (esquire) six years later, he received the King's official *brevet* appointing him *First Painter of the King* on July 1st 1664. Combined with his other offices (such as Director of the newly founded Gobelins factory, which he successfully organized), he received a considerable annual stipend from the Crown as well as fees for individual commissions.[5] Although Richelieu's death and Fouquet's arrest and expulsion from the Academy had impaired Le Brun's career, he had regained Royal favor through the support of Colbert. As a painter his greatest achievements were large-scale decorations, with comparatively few great easel paintings and portraits. His influence on all aspects of design was far-reaching, extending to tapestries, gold and silverware, the settings for court entertainments and ceremonies, as well as the interiors of royal palaces and churches. The royal academicians of the following century were indebted to him as much because of his artistic talents as his success in permanently establishing the academic canons which governed their institution until its abolition.

Le Brun worked vigorously to secure the pre-eminence of the recently established '*Académie Royale de Peinture et Sculpture*'. From 1663 the title of 'Painter of the King' was limited to Academy members. In 1666 he instituted new statutes which strengthened his control and inspired the foundation of the French Academy in Rome, to which his former rival, Charles Errard, was sent as Director. These statutes formalized the Academy's efforts to establish history painting as the ultimate artistic ideal. Unlike his successors, Le Brun was in frequent personal contact with the King. He was consulted directly on major artistic and architectural projects and occasionally included in the royal suite on military campaigns. Le Brun's autocratic style may have alienated some members of the Academy, but for the most part they were united in their admiration and respect for him. In 1667, Le Brun was uniquely honored when his fellow artists chose his audience with the King as the subject of the first *prix de Rome* (an idea he wisely, but perhaps reluctantly, rejected). In the same year he began the series of conferences on the history of art which were to be continued sporadically until the end of the Academy. In the conference on human physiognomy that he gave in 1671 he reaffirmed the old traditions of draughtsmanship, but emphasised the need for direct study of nature. Thereafter the study of the human figure by all students of the Academy was an essential part of their training.

Despite his apparently untramelled power, Le Brun's authority was not unchallenged. In 1675, Roger de Piles and Nicholas Loir sought the appointment of a Director of the Academy. Although they failed in this and Le Brun was elected 'Prince' of the Academy of Saint Luke in Rome for two years running, his power was now threatened by another important group led by Mignard and his patrons. In 1683, Colbert died and Le Brun was faced with the unwelcome duty of requesting Controller-General

FIG. 1 Mignard, *Louis XIV*, Versailles

Louvois, Mignard's principal supporter, to grant his protection to the Academy. In spite of being elected Director and still enjoying the favor of the King, Louvois effectively sabotaged Le Brun's authority. Major commissions were given to his rivals and, without the Superintendent's support, Le Brun's control of the Academy was lost. His considerable wealth, derived from official and private commissions as well as frequent individual grants, had enabled him to buy a substantial country house surrounded by grand gardens where he lived like a great nobleman. With his downfall, the consequent decline in the number and quality of commissions severely diminished his income. To injure him further, Mignard solicited the passage of a statute which ordered that the contents of the studio of the First Painter should revert to the Crown on the death of the holder. This severely affected Le Brun's widow, but although the same law was applied on the death of Mignard himself, it does not appear to have been enforced subsequently.[6]

Le Brun's position was unique and none of his successors as First Painter succeeded in so totally dominating the arts. He had been a very willing instrument in the King and Colbert's plan to gain central control over all aspects of the Fine Arts. His administration of the Gobelins set an example which was followed throughout Europe: in Spain with the foundation of the Royal carpet and tapestry factory, in Saxony and later in several other German states and the Kingdom of the Two Sicilies with the establishment of porcelain factories. Le Brun was invested with almost every honor possible, except, inexplicably, the *Cordon Noir* (the Order of Saint Michel, the second of the *Orders of the King*), which was given to most of his successors and several other artists who had particularly served the Crown.[7]

On Le Brun's death, Mignard's ambition was at last fulfilled and he received all the First Painter's offices within four weeks, by patent of March 1st 1690. Like Le Brun he had made a great fortune, which he passed to his daughter and frequent model. Mignard had achieved his prominent position as an accomplished painter of religious decorations, but much of his income and later reputation derived from his work as a portraitist. As an administrator his tenure of office as First Painter was of little significance as there was virtually no money available for major projects and his age would have made their execution very difficult. Thus his appointment was more a recognition of past successes as well as symbolizing his final triumph over Le Brun.

Mignard was not replaced after his death in 1695 and the position of First Painter remained vacant for twenty years. The Exchequer was bankrupt and the Crown threatened by hostile forces over the succession of Philip V of Spain. Coming after years of conflict with the Netherlands, the war of the Spanish Succession was disastrous for the French economy. Added to this, the sombre influence of the King's morganatic wife, Madame de Maintenon, led Louis XIV [FIG. 1] to abandon most of the artistic and architectural extravagances of earlier years. Madame, the Duchess of Orléans, was to describe the Court as being 'all sadness, boredom and mistrust' – dining there was like being 'in a nun's refectory'. Court balls were still held, but the art of painting received little encouragement, beyond the recording of special historic events such as the reception of the Persian Ambassador in 1715, painted by Antoine Coypel. It was not until the death of the King and the establishment of the Duke of Orléans as Regent that a First Painter was once more appointed.

The choice fell, not surprisingly, on Antoine Coypel, son of the distinguished history painter Noel Coypel (director of the French Academy in Rome from 1673–5), whose patent was dated October 1715. Already the favorite painter of the Regent's father, he had been *First Painter to the Duke of Orléans* since 1688 after coming to the attention of the Court through his work for the *Grande Mademoiselle* at her château at Choisy.[8]

He had been received into the Academy at the age of twenty,[9] and was renowned not only as a painter but also as the designer of a series of medals commemorating the great events of the reign. After completing the ceiling of the Chapel in Versailles he was appointed in 1710, *Director of the paintings and drawings of the King's Cabinet* (Curator of the Royal Collection).[10] However, due to the Crown's bankruptcy there was little opportunity for Coypel to be involved in major artistic projects. Instead he concentrated on cataloguing the Royal collection of drawings, a task continued by his son.

While Court patronage had fallen off after the death of Mignard, the art market itself was slowly changing with increasing numbers of new-rich collectors, many of whom were building grand *hôtels particuliers* in Paris, thus providing alternative sources of commissions and a new direction in taste. Meanwhile the development of auction sales, the appearance of art dealer-collectors such as de Jullienne and the taste for small Dutch or Flemish paintings may have combined to increase the demand for easel paintings. Although André Felibien's formal codification of the hierarchy of genres had further elevated the theoretical status of history painting,[11] private sponsorship was more arbitrary, leaving painters of the *grand genre* dependent for support principally on the Crown and Church.

To be accepted as a history painter it was almost always necessary to have undergone the Academy's strict training in draughtsmanship. The aspirant artist, particularly the history painter, after studying in the Academy's school, entered for the *Grand Prix*, a competition in drawing and painting. The winner of this prize was sent, as a King's Pensioner, to study at the French Academy in Rome. With the bankruptcy of the Crown the winners were not always able to take up this opportunity, as the necessary funds were withheld. Although all the First Painters, with the exception of C. Coypel, spent time in Italy, Le Moyne, who won the prize in 1711 at the height of the war, did not leave until 1724 when he was sponsored by two wealthy patrons and was already a successful, mature artist. Boucher was prevented from going for the same reason, having won the prize in 1724, and had to wait until 1727 before going to Rome, paying his own expenses. On the artist's return he was expected to submit a work to the Academicians for their approval and, if it met the required standards, would be *agréé* as a probationary member, only becoming a full member on presenting his *morceau de réception*, whose subject would be chosen by the First Painter. Several artists who had been *agréé* never actually submitted a reception piece, although it was essential if an artist wished to pursue the conventional route through the ranks of the Academy.

Students of the Academy in both Paris and Rome were subject to teaching methods which encouraged a uniform iconography through the use of recognizable symbols. A painter often had to render a subject with some reference to contemporary history or the prestige of the Monarchy. Aspirants to Royal favor and the First Painters themselves were obviously inclined to interpret their subjects in a form which would improve their standing at Court. Thus it was no coincidence that the decorations at Versailles by Le Brun included great moments in the life of Alexander, whose achievements were thereby compared with those of his Royal master. The constant references to the Aeneid, always a popular subject for French artists, may have been an attempt to parallel the foundation of the French Monarchy by Hugues Capet. Aeneas was the son of the goddess Venus by a Trojan Prince, Anchises. Preselected for his royal blood, he successfully fulfilled his hereditary duty in founding the state of Rome. This legend had obvious attractions for the Bourbon Monarchy and through numerous commissions the Crown associated itself with this story. Le Brun painted the moment of Aeneas' deification, Antoine Coypel and Van Loo the rescue of Anchises by Aeneas from the burning city of Troy, and Le Brun, Antoine Coypel, Boullongne, Van Loo, Boucher and Pierre the moment when Vulcan presents the arms for Aeneas to Venus.

FIG. 2 Van Loo, *Portrait of Louis XV*, Versailles

Just as history paintings could be used to justify the authority of the Monarchy, so could portraits. Some painters, particularly Mignard, liked to disguise a formal portrait in a mythological setting, often casting his patrons in the roles of gods or goddesses. More specifically his successor Antoine Coypel, when painting the four Evangelists for the ceiling of the Chapel at Versailles, also included the Emperor Charlemagne, founder of the Frankish Monarchy and Saint Louis, Louis IX and a direct ancestor of the King.[12] Coypel's reception piece for the Academy was especially direct, an allegory of *Louis XIV Resting in Glory after the Peace of Nimeguen*. Other works by him which reinforced this connection included *History Resting on Time to Write the Life of Louis XIV, while Mercury Presents his Portrait*; *Minerva showing the Temple of Immortality to the child Louis XV*; *The Virtues of Louis XIV*; and an *Allegory on the Death of the Duke of Orléans*. Le Moyne was willing to flatter the Monarchy with such unabashed propaganda as *Louis XV Giving the Peace to Europe*; *Louis XV Surrounded by the Figures of France, Victory and Religion*; and *The Portrait of the King in the Middle of the Assembly of the Gods*.

Coypel's death in 1722 left the post vacant until the appointment of Louis II de Boullongne by Patent of March 21st 1725. This artist, the son of a distinguished painter and younger brother of another, had inherited a substantial fortune. He was also a disciple of Le Brun, had worked in Rome and on his return pursued a highly successful career, being appointed a professor in 1694, Rector in 1717 and Director in 1722. In the same year he was given the *Cordon Noir* and two years later granted hereditary nobility. His appointment as First Painter was as much recognition of the role he and his family had played in the Academy over the previous half-century as of his standing as an artist. While he did not institute any important reforms as First Painter, he strictly enforced the Academy's statutes.[13] Meanwhile, the financial affairs of the Crown were gradually improving and the young Louis XV [FIG. 2], although never as closely involved in the arts as his great-grandfather, was encouraged to increase the number of Royal commissions.[14]

On the death of Boullongne in 1733, François Le Moyne appeared to be his obvious successor. The step-son of the painter Robert Tournières and an ambitious artist, Le Moyne was anxious for public recognition. However, the post of First Painter was also eagerly sought by Jean-François De Troy, with whom Le Moyne had shared the prize in the 1727 competition. Although he actively solicited the title and was supported by the Superintendent, the Duke d'Antin, Le Moyne had to wait another three years until his ceiling for the *Salon d'Hercule* was completed. As recognition of this achievement his patent as First Painter was finally issued on September 30th 1736. By then he had become obsessed with the belief that he had been deliberately ignored and that the honors showered upon Le Brun, which he regarded as his due, had been unjustly withheld. He neglected his administrative responsibilities, became more eccentric in his behaviour and constantly feared persecution. Finally, after only ten months in office, Le Moyne locked himself in a room and, with his horrified friend François Berger hammering on the door, stabbed himself to death with seven blows of a sword.

The death of Le Moyne left a vacancy which was not to be filled for ten years, with the appointment of Charles Coypel, by patent of January 20th 1747. The reasons for the long periods in which the post of First Painter remained vacant (1695–1715, 1736–47 and 1752–62) need investigating. This may have been the result of the Crown's precarious finances, but it is also possible that the Superintendants during these periods may have resented the intrusion of a powerful First Painter and preferred to retain direct control. However, the appointment of a First Painter became automatic from the death of Carle Van Loo in 1765, even during the political crisis of 1789 when the finances of the Crown were in total disorder.

FIG. 3 L. Tocqué, *Seigneur de Tournehem*, Versailles

FIG. 4 J. F. De Troy, *Marquis de Marigny*, Versailles

The influence of the King's mistress, the Marquise de Pompadour, had obtained the appointment of her mother's lover, Charles-François-Paul Le Normand, Seigneur de Tournehem [FIG. 3], as Director-General of Buildings.[15] One of his first decisions was to propose the appointment of Charles-Antoine Coypel as First Painter, beginning a highly successful partnership. Coypel's commitment to the Academy and its teaching mirrored that of Le Brun's, while Tournehem's access to the King ensured their proposals were enacted. One of their first reforms was to increase the price paid for history paintings, and to institute a competition, which they hoped to make an annual event at the Salon.[16] In 1748 they established an admission jury for the Salon, composed of a committee of history painters who would examine 'scrupulously and without passion the paintings presented to adorn the Salon, and, by process of scrutiny, suppress those which do not appear worthy to be put before the eyes of the public'.[17] To further improve the standards of applicants for the *Grand Prix* they founded the *École Royale des Elèves Protégés* in 1747. To ensure that his nephew and successor, Abel Poisson, Marquis de Vandières (better known by his later title of Marquis de Marigny [FIG. 4]), would continue his policies, Le Normand arranged for him to travel to Rome and be properly instructed in the history of art.[18]

Until the appointment of Tournehem and Coypel, the administration of the arts had not been given such capable direction since the death of Le Brun a half century earlier. As First Painter, Coypel was the regular intermediary between the members of the Academy and Le Normand. Coypel was appointed primarily because of his administrative talents and intellectual standing and he became deeply involved in his duties. The most important of these was to oversee work on all the paintings commissioned by the Crown. During his period in office his responsibilities were extended and these became the norm for his successors and their deputies. He transmitted all the requests, proposals and complaints of the members of the Academy; he took responsibility for the distribution of favors, positions, pensions, indemnities, studios and lodgings in the Galleries of the Louvre; he prepared the commissions, indicated the subjects to be treated, and evaluated the work as it progressed. He actively encouraged the intellectual life of the Academy, proposing his friend the Comte de Caylus, a highly educated and sophisticated collector, as an honorary Academician. Both Coypel and Caylus read papers regularly to the Academy and their association strengthened the links between the Academy and leading patrons outside the Court. For example, Coypel honored the intelligent connoisseur in his lecture on the 'Necessity of taking advice' and Caylus, for his part, devoted lectures to the lives of famous artists of the French school, including Claude and Le Moyne.

Tournehem died in November 1751 and Coypel the following June. The new Director-General, the 24-year-old Marigny, waited a decade before recommending the appointment of a First Painter. Such an appointment may have been considered unnecessary as there were comparatively few official commissions of history subjects during the first few years of his directorate. This may have been due to the acute lack of funds, but the absence of a suitable candidate who combined the administrative skills of a Coypel with the artistic talents of a Le Moyne may have led Marigny to delay making a recommendation to the King. With the advantage of his Roman education and possessed of an acute intelligence, Marigny was popular with the Academicians and remained in office until just before the death of Louis XV. His own tastes were for the seductive nudes of Boucher, his sister's favorite painter, Van Loo and Pierre, each of whom was appointed First Painter during his tenure. Neither Van Loo nor Boucher were conventional choices, as both were admired for the pictorial and decorative rather than intellectual qualities of their work. During their tenure the responsibilities of the First Painter were divided, the administrative duties devolving firstly on Bernard Lepicié, Perpetual Secretary and

Historiographer of the Academy. An engraver and professor of 'history, fable and geography' at the *École des Élèves Protegés*, his official responsibilities were limited – he did not play a part in the selection of subjects for commissions. On Lepicié's death in 1755, Marigny chose as his successor the engraver and critic Charles-Nicholas Cochin, who had been his adviser since their celebrated trip to Rome in 1749. Cochin, whose influence was more extensive than Lepicié's, continued to hold this post during the tenure of both Van Loo and Boucher. This radical change in the relationship between the First Painter and the Director-General seems to have been willingly accepted until the appointment of Pierre in 1770.[19]

Carle Van Loo, who was appointed First Painter by a patent of August 6th 1762, came from a dynasty of artists who had achieved prominent positions in several European courts. He had worked at the court of the King of Sardinia in Turin and one of his nephews, Louis-Michel Van Loo, was already First Painter to the King of Spain, while another, Charles-Amedée, became First Painter to the King of Prussia. He had been received into the Academy in 1735, become a professor in 1737 and rector in 1754. Although his reputation as a history painter was questioned, even in his lifetime, he was a particularly popular and respected Professor at the *Élèves Protégés* – among his most outstanding students was Jean-Honoré Fragonard. Baron Grimm, who once called him 'the finest painter in Europe', nonetheless described him as a 'foolish fellow and it was pathetic to hear him talk about painting. All he knew how to do was make fine pictures: he could neither read nor write'.[20]. He was married to a highly successful opera singer, Christina Somis, whom he had met in Turin and was a well-known and popular figure in Parisian society. On his appointment as First Painter he asked to be allowed to retain his teaching post and soon resigned the Directorship of the Academy. Both these positions entailed administrative functions which would have inhibited his commitment to teaching and painting, although he was content to enjoy the prestige of First Painter. At the *Élèves Protégés* he organised a strict regimen for his students; they read from Bossuet and texts from antiquity from 7.30 am until 9.00 am and then drew until luncheon, when Van Loo would inspect their efforts. In the evening they drew from the human figure, after an afternoon of studying pictures in the Royal Collection. They ended their day with more reading, all the while living at the expense of the King, attended by two footmen each.[21]

Van Loo died after only three years in office and the appointment of Boucher, by patent of September 8th 1765, followed within a month. By the time of his appointment as First Painter he was being frequently attacked by Salon critics of whom the most hostile was Denis Diderot. This writer condemned what he considered to be the lack of moral or dramatic content in Boucher's work and abhorred his influence on younger artists of the French school. Diderot's attacks cannot have encouraged Boucher, but he carried on painting in spite of them and when he died there was an uncompleted work on his easel. He was not remembered as a particularly assiduous administrator – Diderot went as far as accusing him of causing the students at the Academy to starve through his negligence. Although Boucher had continued to enjoy the support of his old patrons, his appointment did not influence the direction of French artistic development. The rococo style was rapidly falling into public disfavour and the appointment of Boucher was an indication of how the aging King's tastes were out of step with those of private collectors.

Boucher's death in May 1770 was followed by the appointment of Jean-Baptiste-Marie Pierre, by a patent of June 4th of the same year. This artist had had a very successful official career since winning the *Grand Prix* in 1734. He was received into the Academy in 1742, became a professor in 1744 and assistant rector in 1768. Diderot was particularly scathing of what he perceived as Pierre's desire for social advancement as well as, unjustly, his ability as a painter. Although Pierre's personal wealth made it

FIG. 5 J. S. Duplessis, *Louis XVI*, Versailles

FIG. 6 J. B. Greuze, *Count d'Angiviller*, Metropolitan Museum of Art

unnecessary for him to work and he was not as prolific as Boucher, he had several excellent students, including Bachelier, Durameau, Taraval, J. B. Restout, N. B. Lepicié and M. Garnier. However, by the late 1760's his style was out of fashion and his appointment as First Painter may have reflected his personal standing at Court as well as his past reputation as an artist. Rather than adapt his style to conform with developing neo-classicism, he virtually abandoned painting and instead dedicated himself to his administrative role, encouraging a new generation of history painters.

The accession of Louis XVI [FIG. 5] brought the appointment of a particularly influential Director-General, Charles-Claude de Flahaut de la Billarderie, Count d'Angiviller [FIG. 6], who held the post until the Revolution. D'Angiviller's full title was Director and Organizer General of the Royal Buildings, Gardens, Arts, Academies and Factories, and was particularly close to the new King, having served him as a *Gentilhomme de la Manche des Enfants de France*. Criticised by some artists for confiding too much administrative responsibility to Pierre, it is hardly surprising that they worked so well together. Pierre had arranged the marriage of his niece to the son of the Foreign Minister, Charles, Count of Vergennes.[22] He and d'Angiviller were thus on more equal terms socially than any of his contemporaries. Pierre had received the Order of the King in 1762 and in addition to holding the post of First Painter of the King, with a salary recently raised to 6,000 livres, was also First Painter of the Duke of Orléans with a similar emolument.[23] In 1778 he was appointed Perpetual Director of the Academy by a special Royal dispensation and in 1783 chief curator of the new 'museum' planned for the Louvre. A very capable administrator, Pierre was a staunch defender of the rights of the Academicians and successfully resisted an attempt to make the election of Professors subject to Royal approval. Neither did he attempt to dictate subject matter to the members of the Academy and he abandoned his prerogative of choosing the subject of an artist's reception piece. After consulting the artists he would submit the 'subjects capable of being executed' to d'Angiviller, who would formally assign the commissions. However, in much of his administration he was arrogant and dictatorial and at one time suggested that no son of the 'vile populace' or anyone with a physical deformity should be admitted to the Academy's school.[24]

It may have been a source of frustration to Pierre, that, in spite of his otherwise excellent relationship with d'Angiviller, the latter still deferred to Vien in artistic matters during the 1770's and 1780's, when Vien's style was more fashionable.[25] Nonetheless, between 1776 and 1790 d'Angiviller, with Pierre's and Vien's encouragement, managed to obtain from the Treasury the sum of 590,454 livres for academic commissions, although this was less than Louis XIV had spent in the same period a century earlier. Pierre ensured that many of the younger history painters obtained pensions from the Crown on a larger scale. He also encouraged d'Angiviller to request patents of nobility and the Order of the King for members of the Academy. During his tenure history painting was considerably revived. However, there was no consistency of style as there had been forty years earlier when Pierre himself was in his prime. While a few artists such as Doyen, Durameau and Berthelemy were working in a romantic and emotional style still reminiscent of the rococo, David, Regnault and Peyron and their disciples followed the harder, neo-classical style developed by Vien.

Pierre died on May 15th 1789 and Vien was appointed to succeed him by a patent issued two days later. Married to a successful painter of flowers, Vien had returned from Rome in 1781, where he had been Director at the Palazzo Mancini, to be appointed Rector of the Academy. Unlike most of the other First Painters, Vien continued as an active painter, in spite of his great age, until the abolition of the Academy. Vien's period in office as First Painter was short-lived and he had no opportunity to exercise any important administrative functions. The Bastille fell on July 14th, two months after his appointment, and the King and Queen moved to Paris, taking the oath to the Constitution a year later. The Monarchy was abolished by a vote of the Assembly on September 21st 1792, making the post of First Painter redundant, and the Academy was dissolved in the following year.[26] Vien, a Count and Senator of the Empire, died on March 27th 1809 aged 92; David, now himself First Painter to the Emperor, remarked when he heard the news 'our father has ceased to live'.

The present-day view of the eighteenth century is inevitably colored by our own perspective of history and this is particularly true of French painting in the period. The passage of time and a fundamental change in the way we look at painting has resulted in a very different view of artistic accomplishment. Unencumbered by the belief in the importance of the hierarchy of genres that prevailed throughout the period of this exhibition, we are able to compare the works of Le Brun and Watteau, Boucher and Chardin, Vien and Greuze, and arrive at very different conclusions from those of their contemporaries. Neither are we bound to the view that the art of painting should, in its most sublime form, uplift our morals and elevate the mind. Antoine Coypel's belief that 'the hand, however, is what contributes least to the excellence of this art' (i.e. 'the most perfect form of painting')[27] would find few adherents in the next century or our own. Baron Grimm's attack on Van Loo because he only knew how to paint 'fine pictures' is probably unintelligible to the modern critic. Rousseau actually considered that the plastic arts had failed the *Age of Reason*, since he felt they contributed neither to personal morality nor public virtue, while Voltaire found much of eighteenth-century history painting 'effete' in comparison with that of the reign of Louis XIV.[28] The recent Diderot exhibition in Paris demonstrated that some of that writer's artistic preferences might have more support from the modern audience than they would have had from his contemporaries. Unlike the Salon jury we no longer expect art to be 'worthy', nor do we judge it according to its success in 'immortalizing' political institutions.

Although there has recently been substantial revision of the Goncourt brothers views on eighteenth-century French art, their priorities and preferences still command wide support, particularly in the United States. They took the view that the execution and beauty of the work is of paramount importance, subjugating completely the choice of subject matter or artistic conception. Since they largely ignored works which attempted a deeper response to the moral, religious and political questions of the time and instead selected for consideration artists or paintings whose impact is much more immediate, their response to French eighteenth-century painting is hardly surprising. The failure of the French academic establishment in the later nineteenth century to keep up with contemporary artistic developments led some critics, the Goncourt's included, to disparage history painting in general. While the present taste for scenes of contemporary life, natural landscapes and still lifes reflects an interest in the 'painterly' techniques we admire in the Impressionists, few try to understand the importance of the *grand genre* to the eighteenth-century audience. Although one third of all the paintings exhibited at the Salon were history subjects, later collectors have largely ignored them.

Whether the First Painters themselves, after the downfall of Le Brun, had any real impact on the direction of French painting still needs investigating. Le Brun had initiated the strict regulation of the Academy which was continued by Boullongne, Charles Coypel and Pierre. This resulted in the uniform teaching methods which affected all Academy students and the perpetuation of the supremacy of history painting. There is little doubt that without the active intervention of Charles Coypel and Pierre and the support of Tournehem, Marigny and d'Angiviller, the importance and number of history paintings would have substantially declined by the end of the century. Neither Le Moyne, Van Loo, nor Boucher follow the model of the other First Painters who were as much involved in administration as in painting. However, the post was perceived as a great honor and even an artist as successful as Boucher was sufficiently proud of the title to write *PP du Ry* after his name.[29] We do not suggest in this exhibition that these ten artists were equally able, although all of them produced outstanding works. We have attempted to indicate the range of French history painting by the selection of at least one work from each of the First Painters, although most of the paintings were produced before the artists' appointment. The inventory of paintings in US public collections shows the very limited representation in this country of all the artists other than Boucher. The bibliography of the latter is very extensive, but little has been published on Mignard, Boullongne, the Coypels, Pierre or Vien. Even in France it is difficult to see pictures by some of these artists without visiting the provincial museums or Parisian churches, many of which are poorly lit and the pictures untouched since their installation. Although the 'Age of Louis XV' exhibition presented a wide cross-section of eighteenth-century French painting to the American public,[30] until very recently French history painting from the mid-seventeenth to late eighteenth centuries has been virtually ignored in this country. This exhibition is a modest attempt to redress this neglect.

Notes

[1] History painting was generally referred to as the *grand genre*. It included subjects from the Bible, the lives of the Saints, Greek and Roman history, the works of writers such as Homer, Virgil and Ovid and more recent authors such as Petrarch and Tasso. The eighteenth-century history painters also sometimes chose subjects from contemporary writers such as La Fontaine and Moliere, an innovation critized by many conservatives. Scenes from more recent history also became popular with French artists as the century progressed.

[2] From Boucher's patent of September 8th 1765.

[3] The Academy had been founded in 1648 at the instigation of Colbert to give the Crown control of the arts and was established with a strict hierarchy of officers – Director, Rector, Chancellor, Professors, Assistant-Professors, Secretary, members and *agréé* members. Only Academicians could exhibit at the Salon, held originally in April but by the eighteenth century from the Feast of Saint Louis on August 25th. Initially they had lasted ten days but were gradually extended to thirty days by the end of the Monarchy. The exhibitions were held biannually from 1737 in the Salon Carré of the Louvre, spilling into the neighbouring galleries. There were sometimes as many as 450 entries, of which about one third were history paintings, some artists including more than a dozen works. They were tremendously popular with the educated public, the annual catalogues, or *livrets*, selling as many as 20,000 copies by the end of the Monarchy. These listed all the artists exhibiting, in order of precedence in the Academy, and included the title of each painting, sculpture, drawing or engraving.

[4] Le Brun did not become Director until nineteen years after his appointment but retained effective control of the Academy through his post as Chancellor for life.

[5] In 1666 his stipend amounted to 12,000 livres per annum.

[6] This information by written communication of M. Pierre Rosenberg, Chief Curator of the Department of Paintings of the Louvre.

[7] An applicant had to prove four generations of nobility but could do this by acquiring an honorary post such as *sécretaire du Roi* (of whom there were several hundred) which conferred equivalent lifetime nobility and could be purchased by, or was given to, an aspirant courtier. In 1785 several living artists were included in the Roll of the Order (Cochin, Pierre, Pigalle, Silvestre, Vien and Larcheveque) out of a total membership of only eighty-five. Although all the First Painters were ennobled, none ever received or acquired a noble territory which would have given them the title of Marquis, Count, Viscount or Baron. Only Vien, in the next century, received the hereditary title of Count from Napoleon, shortly before his death.

[8] The *Grande Mademoiselle* (as she was known to her contemporaries) was the Duchess of Montpensier, eldest daughter of the King's uncle, Gaston, Duke of Orléans, and heiress to the immense fortune of her mother.

[9] Charles-Antoine Coypel was also received at a very early age, twenty-one; however, few artists were admitted before their twenty-eighth birthday.

[10] He resigned this post to his son, Charles, in 1719.

[11] The hierarchy was history painting, portraiture, genre, still-life and landscape painting. Prices paid for pictures followed this same pattern with history painters receiving the highest fees.

[12] Stories from the life of Saint Louis became even more popular with the revival of interest in French history encouraged by d'Angiviller in the last two decades of the Monarchy.

[13] An example of this was his decision to have the elder brother of the portraitist Jean-Marc Nattier expelled from the Academy because of his corrupt morals. The unfortunate man subsequently committed suicide in prison by cutting his throat.

[14] To revive history painting, Boullongne, in conjunction with the Superintendant, the Duke d'Antin, planned a competition for the members of the Academy. This was open to any academician, who could choose his own subject, with a prize of 5,000 livres, and attracted entries from Le Moyne, J. F. De Troy (these two great rivals shared the money prize), Cazes, Favannes, Restout, Collin de Vermont, N. Coypel, Massé, Courtin, Dieu, Galloche and C. A. Coypel (whose painting of *Perseus and Andromeda* was purchased by the King).

[15] Tournehem had been responsible for the education of his mistress' daughter, Jeanne Poisson, and had given her in marriage to his nephew, the Seigneur d'Etiolles. Soon after becoming the King's mistress she was created Marquise, and later Duchesse, de Pompadour.

[16] The competition of 1747 was modelled on that of 1727 with eleven artists, selected by the First Painter, competing for the prize. Each were allowed to choose their own subject, but all inevitably selected a story from mythology or Greek and Roman history. At the same time the scale of prices for history paintings was revised: 6,000 livres for the large 'machines' of 18 to 22 square feet; 5,000 livres for pictures of 13 to 17 square feet and 4,000 livres for smaller paintings of 9 to 12 square feet.

[17] *Procès-Verbaux de l'Académie royale de peinture et de sculpture* (1648–1793), publ. by A. de Montaiglon, 1875–92, Paris, vol. VI, 108, cited Jean Locquin, *La Peinture d'Histoire en France de 1747 a 1785*, Laurens, Paris, 1912, p. 7.

[18] Vandières was a recently ennobled bourgeois, the brother of the Marquise de Pompadour, and had had the *survivance* of Le Normand's office since 1746.

[19] Cochin was highly critical of Pierre, who disliked him and objected strongly to Cochin being appointed a Royal councillor and being given a pension from the Crown (*Procès-Verbaux*, op. cit., vol. VIII, 249, cited by Locquin, pp. 43–4).

[20] Quoted by Jacques Thuillier and Albert Châtelet, *French Painting from Le Nain to Fragonard*, Skira, Geneva, 1964, p. 187.

[21] Georges Wildenstein, *Fragonard*, Phaidon, 1960, pp. 5–6. Since the Crown was frequently in arrears with its grants to the School, the students were often subsidized by Van Loo himself.

[22] Pierre gave his niece a dowry worth the immense sum of 60,000 livres in rents (Letter of Dandré-Bardon to the Academy of Marseille, January 9th 1783, published in *Histoire documentaire de l'Académie de peinture et sculpture de Marseille*, Paris, 1889–90, vol. I, 311, cited by Locquin, p. 43).

[23] Pierre was Director of the Gobelins and Savonnerie factories, honorary Director of the Marseilles Academy, honorary member of the Royal Academy of Architecture and associate member of the Academies of Saint Petersburg, Vienna and Kassel.

[24] L. Courajod, *L'Ecole royale des Élèves Protégés*, Paris, 1874, 138 and following, cited by Locquin, p. 43.

[25] Locquin, p. 47.

[26] With the restoration, the *Institut* created by the Constitution of 5 fructidor an III (August 22nd 1795) was reorganized into the *Institut Royal* by an ordinance of March 21st 1816. This was composed of four Academies, of which the Royal Academy of Fine Arts was the most junior. The title of Academician, which conferred none of the privileges enjoyed under the *Ancien Régime*, was limited to fourteen painters, eight sculptors, eight architects (the Royal Academy of Architecture being amalgamated with the Fine Arts), four engravers and six musicians (also included for the first time). None of the distinctions of Director, Chancellor, Rector or Professors were preserved, although there was a category of *Académiciens libres* who were mainly noblemen with an artistic interest (one of them, Turpin de Crissé, was himself a distinguished painter). There was also a category of foreign associates (who included Canova, Benjamin West and the aged composer Salieri) and some minor artists as *correspondans*. A year later Baron Gérard was given the purely nominal title of 'First Painter of the King' which entailed no particular responsibility beyond being required to record certain historic occasions for posterity (such as the Coronation of Charles X). Of the fourteen painters nominated to the new Academy, four had been full members (Van Spaendonck, Regnault, Vivant-Denon and Le Barbier) and two *agréé* members (Taunay and Carle Vernet) of the former Royal Academy. David, the regicide living in exile in Brussels who had been appointed 'First Painter to the Emperor' in 1804, was not included.

[27] Quoted by Thuillier and Châtelet, op. cit, p. 143.

[28] Philip Conisbee, *Painting in Eighteenth-Century France*, Cornell University Press, 1981, p. 91.

[29] This can be seen following the signature on *L'heureux pêcheur* of 1769, Private Collection, New York.

[30] Held in Toledo, Ohio, and Chicago, Illinois, 1975–6.

In addition to the works cited above, the following general works were referred to:

Edmond and Jules de Goncourt, *L'art du dix-huitieme siècle*, 3 vols, Paris, Academie Goncourt, 1884.

Marc Furcy-Raymaud, *Les Premiers Peintres du Roi*, in Archive de l'Art Français, Paris, 1914, pp. 207–14.

Louis Reau, *L'Histoire de la Peinture Française au XVIII siècle*, 2 vols, Paris, Van Oest, 1925.

Louis Dimier, *L'Histoire de la Peinture Française, 1627–90*, 2 vols, Paris, Van Oest, 1926.

Louis Dimier, *Les peintres français du XVIII siècle*, 2 vols, Paris, Van Oest, 1928.

David Wakefield, *French Eighteenth-Century Painting*, London, Gordon Fraser, 1984.

Religious Painting in the Age of Reason

by Philip Conisbee, M.A.

FIG. 1 Boucher, *Woman with a Cat*, New Orleans Museum of Art

'The *savants* – I beg their pardons, the *philosophes* – are insupportable. Superficial, overbearing and fanatic; they preach incessantly, and their avowed doctrine is atheism; you would not believe how openly – Don't wonder, therefore, if I should return a Jesuit. Voltaire himself does not satisfy them ... *Tout le monde est philosophe* – when I grow very sick of this last nonsense, I go and compose myself at the Chartreuse [*sic*], where I am almost tempted to prefer Lesueur to every painter I know.'[1]

Horace Walpole's letter reflects his experience of the 'polite' and fashionable world of the literary and intellectual salons he frequented on his visits to Paris during the 1760's. If few Frenchmen would joke about being Jesuits at this time (after much bitter controversy, the Order had been expelled from France in 1764), Walpole would not have been alone in visiting the great Carthusian monastery of Paris (demolished in 1796), and in deriving solace from the works of one of the celebrated religious painters of the seventeenth century, Eustache Lesueur (1615–55; the paintings, illustrating the life of St Bruno, are now in the Louvre).

Walpole's image of cultivated Parisian society of the eighteenth century remains very much the one handed down to us by positivist and materialist historians of the nineteenth century. The visual aspect of this culture can be found in the witty interpretations of erotic mythology by Boullongne, Le Moyne, Pierre and Boucher in the present exhibition, or in Boucher's light-hearted scenes such as *Woman with a Cat* [FIG. 1]; in the searching psychological perceptions of a portraitist such as Quentin de la Tour; in the moralizing view of women, children and their occupations by Chardin in his genre scenes; in the moral-sentimental domestic dramas of Greuze; and, on a more 'elevated' plane, in the moral alternative to Christianity sought in the history and philosophy of the Greco-Roman world by neo-classical history painters during the last four decades of the century (anticipated, here, by Lebrun's *Hercules* (no. 1) and Van Loo's *Aeneas Carrying Anchises* (no. 12).

But if enlightened philosophy played a significant part in the cultural life of the eighteenth century – and with nineteenth- and twentieth-century hindsight, its great historical importance becomes more evident than perhaps it was even to the majority of educated Frenchmen of the day – the Church, in all its material, political, intellectual and sentimental manifestations, maintained a far more dominant ideology throughout society, from the Royal court at Versailles, to the fashionable faubourgs of Paris, to the cathedral cities of the provinces, to the remote hamlet, with its down-at-heel curé.

The fundamental role of religious imagery as an aid to devotion was little questioned in the eighteenth century, if at all. There was a varied market for such imagery, supplied by an almost equal variety of artists throughout France: the printmakers of the Rue Saint-Jacques in Paris produced thousands of cheap cuts representing the many saints, or subjects such as the *Pietà*, for itinerant vendors in Paris and the rest of France; they also made finer engravings, to insert into breviaries, for example; hack painters did ex-votos and religious banners for local communities; the wealthier and more important churches and monasteries would display altar pieces made by local masters, or such works might be ordered from the more famous artists who worked in the capital; all manner of painters produced religious pictures, and not least the privileged history painters of the Royal Academy.

Of course all the First Painters to the King were of this latter type. All of them were active as religious painters, and in many cases some of their most important works were executed for churches.

It is generally true that history painters were more ready to work for a church early in their careers, rather than later. The younger and less established artist needed publicity more than an older one, and a church was the one place where his art would be on long-term public display. Certainly, before the establishment of regular Salon exhibitions in 1737, there was little other opportunity for artistic talents to be assessed publicly at all. Thus, among future First Painters, the young Le Moyne produced an important cycle of works on the life of Christ for the Cordeliers of Amiens as his first major commission in 1717 (now at Sens, Cathedral and Seminary); in the late 1740's the young Vien, still a student in Rome, won a large commission to supply altarpieces on the life of St Martha for the conventual church of Sainte-Marthe, Tarascon (still *in situ*). Working for the Church was not all that well-paid, however, whereas working for the Crown or for some wealthy private patron was lucrative.

Private collectors were interested in religious works too, but if not for a chapel they would be small in scale, such as preparatory sketches, models, or reduced versions or copies of large-scale church works. There are several such works in this exhibition, like Carle Van Loo's *Noli Me Tangere* (no. 13), which belonged to the sculptor and woodcarver, Cayeux. At the sale of his effects in 1769 there were some three dozen such small-scale religious works of the Italian and French seventeenth- and eighteenth-century schools. Such a collector certainly valued his religious pictures as works of art, but, of course, their subject matter was also morally exemplary, and may equally reflect the owner's piety.

It is easily forgotten that even Watteau made a few religious works and, according to his friend and biographer, Caylus, was painting a *Crucifixion* for the curé of Nogent at the time of his death in 1721. Watteau's teacher, Claude Gillot, that inventive illustrator above all of theatre scenes, made a large quantity of drawings on the life of Christ, of which Huquier engraved and published in 1732 a series illustrating the Passion. There are many more examples of such 'forgotten' religious works we could cite.

When Charles Coypel wrote[2] that his father, Antoine, by the eloquence of his religious works, 'wished through the eyes to transmit to the heart impressions of the truest morality', he was speaking for all makers of religious art and their patrons in the seventeenth and eighteenth centuries. The most extreme (and, significantly as such, Jesuit) case for the power of religious imagery and decoration had already been made by Jean Crasset in 1679:

> The magnificence of our churches and the decoration of our altars serve well to excite the piety of the faithful. Because spiritual things only enter our minds through material senses, we need external objects to help us conceive the grandeur of God and to impress feelings of respect for the mysteries of our religion. At least, it cannot be denied that common people, whose number is incomparably greater than that of the learned and the spiritual, are excited to honour and to praise God by the rich ornaments of our churches. These spacious temples, these well-decorated altars, these august ceremonies, these rich and precious vestments, all these gold and silver vases, all these well-wrought images contribute not a little to maintaining the majesty of our Sacraments, and to impressing respect for holy things. There are few people who do not feel more devotion in praying to God in a grand and well-decorated church, than in a poor, dirty and neglected place. Oh, how great God is, you say, when you enter a great church! Oh, how rich he is! Oh, how Holy! How powerful! And how terrible! *Vere Deus est in loco isto.* Truly, God is in this place.[3]

A Jansenist might have preferred a more austere devotional environment, and later in the century attitudes to church design in general were affected by the neo-classical preference for noble simplicity over elaborate ornament. But the churches of eighteenth-century France presented a rich spectacle indeed, and the importance of religious imagery was never put in doubt. When in 1705 the Company of Goldsmiths made its annual May donation of a painting to the church of Notre-Dame in Paris, *The Departure of Paul from Miletus* (Louvre, Paris) by Louis Galloche, a broadsheet *Explanation* was issued, asserting its function and some of its merits:

> The most noble object of painting being the edification of Christians, its chosen subjects should be such as to touch their hearts, and to excite them to piety.... You will see that the painter has tried to respond to the zeal and the piety of the Goldsmiths, who with respect offer this picture to the Virgin, according to their worthy custom. The artist hopes that his studies have provided him with expressions capable of inspiring in spectators an ardour similar to that shown by St Paul, in satisfying the commands of the Lord, as well as the respectful tenderness which we should feel for those whom his providence has chosen to lead us along the path of salvation, such as we see in these first Christians of Miletus and Ephesus. [4]

To take one other example, Charles Coypel published a newspaper notice and a pamphlet in 1729 describing his huge *Ecce Homo* painted in the church of the Oratoire (destroyed), which showed 'such a grand and touching event, so as to move the spectators, and lead them to indulge reflections worthy of the place in which the painting is situated'. [5]

The two relatively 'popular' testimonies of Galloche and Coypel do reflect the attitudes to religious art expressed in the more academic essays and treatises of the time. But if the academic theorists devote relatively little discussion to religious painting specifically, it was probably because in their minds this type of subject was simply a part of the genre of history painting in general. Roger de Piles, in his widely-read *Cours de peinture par principes* (1708, and later editions), expressed the opinion that religious works should above all be intelligible to the spectator, founded on the Scriptures or on ecclesiastical history, and should not involve any complex allegory. Moreover, the religious painting was a particularly noble work: 'As nothing is more holy, grander, nor more enduring than the mysteries of our religion, they cannot be treated in too majestic a style'. [6] The Abbé du Bos, in his influential *Réflexions critiques sur la poésie et sur la peinture* (1719, and later editions) was opposed to the invention of allegorical devices for religious painting. When necessary, a figure of Faith or Hope was permissible, but when it came to 'the mysteries, miracles and dogmas of our religion', as far as possible historical truth should be the aim of the artist, and 'his imagination not allowed to wander'. [7] The religious works of the First Painters in this exhibition all conform to this direct presentation of theme.

A perusal of the Salon catalogues of the eighteenth century shows that all history painters worked on religious commissions, which were evidently plentiful. Of course many such works, even by Academicians, were never seen at the Salon in Paris, but were sent off directly to their destinations. A variety of religious works, from mural and ceiling decorations, to altarpieces, to images for cloisters, sacristies or refectories, and so on, were in constant demand for the thousands of churches and hundreds of monasteries all over the kingdom. If new church building, in Paris and the provinces, was not undertaken as often as in the most expansionist seventeenth century, it was not because of the spread of enlightened rationalism. Rather, it was a matter of the relative shortage of money for such projects, and because the embellishment of earlier churches was continuing. Examples would be the magnificent refurbishment of the medieval Parisian church of Saint-Merry during the seventeenth and eighteenth centuries, or of the fact that two of the most impressive ensembles of eighteenth-century church art at Saint-Roch and Saint-Sulpice are to be found in buildings whose construction was begun in the previous century, and only completed during the eighteenth century as funds would allow. These three churches are still important repositories of eighteenth-century art, but subsequent destructions and depredations, especially during the Revolution of 1789, mean that they are now but poor reminders of their *ancien régime* splendor.

During the second half of the century, such magnificent schemes of decoration were becoming the objects of criticism – not only from free-thinkers, but also from artistically informed commentators, who were affected by the rising Neo-classical taste for purer and simpler forms of architecture, painting and decoration. We can trace the influence of enlightened philosophy in some socially-aware critics, who thought that the money spent on rich church decoration might be better employed on charitable relief for the poor and suffering. A commentator in 1782 deplored the 'useless magnificence' of Saint-Sulpice, where 'the sumptuous edifice cost enormously, without any real advantage to humanity'.[8] Already in 1765 the author of one of the best guide-books to Paris lamented the recent refurbishment of Saint-Merry (with a scheme of decoration which remains more-or-less intact to this day, and which involved two of our First Painters, Charles-Antoine Coypel and Van Loo, who each supplied altarpieces), which he felt destroyed the 'magnificent simplicity' of the medieval architecture. At Saint-Roch (where a major ceiling and a major altarpiece were executed respectively by Pierre and, later, Vien), at Saint-Sulpice (where Le Moyne painted a cupola, and Le Moyne, Pierre and Van Loo supplied altarpieces) and at the Oratoire (where Charles-Antoine Coypel painted his *Ecce Homo*), this same commentator recalled with regret the austere rule of St Bernard in the Middle Ages, when the arts of luxury were banned from holy places. His words also embody the social concerns of Enlightenment thought, when he says: 'How many good families, reduced to poverty, would have been supported or relieved?'[9]

For all that Neo-classical critics came to view with disapproval the more lavish and scenographic sequences of architectural, painted and sculptural decoration in churches like Saint-Roch and Saint-Sulpice, and for all that the Enlightenment brought about a new social awareness, there is no reason to suppose that the considerable efforts of clergy, patrons and artists were ineffective in promoting their religious ideology, and also in enhancing the reputation of Paris as the artistic capital of Europe, north of the Alps. Contemporary engravings of church interiors usually show not only devout worshippers and the beggars who frequented churches, but also interested visitors, guide-book in hand, perhaps pointing out some feature to a companion. The popularity of artistic guidebooks to Paris is attested by their frequent editions in the eighteenth century, and the modern reader cannot but be struck by the number of churches and monasteries in the capital, and the proud enumeration of their extensive decorations.

If the demand for religious art of all kinds is one indicator of the positive vitality of religious life in eighteenth-century France, the intense theological debates of the century are another. While Louis XIV's 1685 Revocation of the Edict of Nantes (an edict of Henri IV in 1598, which granted Protestants various rights and liberties) effectively drove any Protestant opposition from French shores, his destruction of the great Jansenist abbey of Port-Royal in 1710 (after decades of harassment and restriction) only drove the austere moral and theological conceptions of Jansenism underground. It was the Jesuits, afraid of losing their dominance in matters of education and religion, and who were the chief enemies of Jansenism on doctrinal grounds, who influenced the restrictive religious policies of Louis XIV and his devout inner circle. The Jansenist 'party' was not to be avenged until late in the reign of Louis XV, when the Jesuits were eventually expelled from France, after decades of further political and nationalistic religious strife.[10]

The austere concept of life of the Jansenists, their repudiation of the efficacy of the human will, their beliefs in predestination and the exclusive importance of divine grace, and their close study of the Scriptures, brought them close to the spirit of Protestantism. Their conception of art in the seventeenth century was also austere, favoring close adherence to the text of the Scriptures, realism of observation, and an avoidance of sensuous or sophisticated visual effects. The artist who best expressed their aesthetic in

FIG. 2 J. Jouvenet, *The Last Rites*, Louvre

the seventeenth century was Philippe de Champaigne (1602–74), whose later works completely reject the rich effects of color and texture, the movement, ecstasy and radiance of full Baroque art, in favor of a more sober and lucid kind of observation, restrained color, and more rigid design. This austere realist strain is ever present in French seventeenth- and eighteenth-century art, particularly in the cases of artists who did not travel to Italy for part of their training. The sensuous and coloristic Baroque style was very much associated with the Jesuits, stemming as it did from the church decorations orchestrated by Gian'Lorenzo Bernini and his followers in seventeenth-century Rome. It is sometimes possible to identify a taking of sides on the part of different French painters in relation to these two aesthetic approaches, but the circumstances and the physical contexts of specific commissions need always to be considered.

The two painters whose reputations were above all founded on religious commissions in our period were Jean Jouvenet (1644–1717) [FIG. 2] and his nephew and pupil, Jean Restout (1692–1768). Neither went to Italy, and it seems that they did sometimes wilfully reject ultramontane manners in their art. Restout especially is discussed here, because he was recognized as the leading specialist in religious painting in the mid-eighteenth century, although he was not a First Painter to the King. Indeed, his unorthodox sympathies may have barred him from consideration for such an official honor. Restout had jansenist leanings, which are reflected in the fact that during a period of renewed controversy over this issue he agreed to paint the portraits of several clergymen of that persuasion: the Abbé Tournus, confessor of the highly controversial Deacon François de Pâris; a lost double portrait of the two, known through engravings; and perhaps a deathbed portrait of Pâris himself.

François de Pâris (1690–1727) was a saintly reformer, who shared the abject poverty of his parishioners in a poor part of Paris. He was devoted to pastoral care, and adored the simple Christ of the Gospels and the Passion. After the death of Pâris in 1727, his tomb in the churchyard of Saint-Médard became a center of popular devotion, and a number of miraculous healings supposedly took place. There and elsewhere in Paris a somewhat hysterical cult developed, involving its participants in miracles, visions, physical convulsions and divine visitations. Such uncontrollable manifestations of popular piety could not be tolerated by the Crown nor by the Church authorities (in the person of successive Archbishops of Paris), so the '*convulsionnaires*', as they were known, were suppressed, and the cemetery of Saint-Médard closed in 1732. The cause, however, was taken up by one Louis-Basile Carré de Montgeron, who in the same cemetery had been converted from scepticism to religious belief. In a substantial book[11] he published detailed eyewitness and medical accounts of the principal curative miracles, and also a defense of Deacon Pâris's rejection of the Papal Bull *Unigenitus*. Pâris was a well-known follower of Pasquier Quasnel, a Jansenist whose *Moral Reflections on the New Testament* (new edition, 1699) found considerable popular support in France, but which was condemned as heretical in the Bull issued by Pope Clement XI in 1713. Acceptance of rejection of this Bull was a contentious, divisive and painful issue of conscience for the French clergy of all ranks, not least because it raised the old issue of papal authority and the relative independence of the Gallican church. The political and religious implications of the dispute lingered on into the middle decades of the century. The political dimension of the issue was the degree to which the French Church, and indeed the Crown, should owe allegiance and obeisance to the Pope in Rome, and to his authority in spiritual and temporal matters. Needless to say, the Jesuits were seen by many as sinister instruments of papal authority.

The Parlement of Paris (and Deacon Pâris came from a parliamentarian family, as did his defender, Carré de Montgeron; Montgeron's tutor had once been Abbé Tournus, confessor of Pâris) was traditionally at odds with the Crown on numerous political and legal issues, and also took a position of opposition to Rome, the Bull, and the Jesuits, although probably more out of political expediency than any Jansenist commitment. Carré de Montgeron's book was explicit in its patriotic attacks on Rome's threat to the powers of the French Crown, and on the Jesuits as the moving force behind the Bull *Unigenitus*. He argued that the miracles at Saint-Médard, through the intercession of Deacon Pâris, were 'the voice of God', and sent as signs of divine rejection of the Bull. In a sense Carré de Montgeron's error was to contrive to present his volume directly to Louis XV in 1737, without receiving permission to do so. But as he explained in his prefatory address to the king, its oppositional content would never have passed the Royal censors. For his trouble, Carré de Montgeron spent the rest of his life in various prisons, and died in one, at Valence, in 1754. This would be reason enough, however, to explain the fact that although Restout made the interesting illustrations to the book in question, he, and his engraver, retained their anonymity. Nevertheless, to be connected with such a contentious topical issue does surely indicate a commitment on the part of the artist, for all that he had the elevated standing of a Professor at the Royal Academy. His illustrations, for which some of the original drawings survive, show the churchyard of Saint-Médard with devotees at the tomb of Pâris, and a series of 'before and after' scenes of those cured by the miracles, rendered in an appropriately realistic idiom.

If in their different manifestations the long-lasting dispute over the Bull *Unigenitus*, and the later even more nationalistic issue of the expulsion of the Jesuits from France, were simply the most famous theological conflicts of eighteenth-century France, they probably occupied contemporary minds more vividly than the threats offered to religious orthodoxy by enlightened and rationalist tendencies of thought, at least until the 1760's and succeeding decades. Two great altarpieces painted for Saint-Roch in 1767, Gabriel-François Doyen's *Intercession of St Genevieve* and Vien's *Preaching of St Denis*, may assert specifically Gallican values just after the expulsion of the Jesuits, by depicting saints especially revered in Parisian and in French national life respectively.

To explore the theological disputes of eighteenth-century France is to ask many more questions than can be answered in a short essay, and would in any case better be the task of a historian deeply versed in the complex religious and political history of the times. Much more primary research needs to be done before we can confidently define the theological significance of individual works of art, or even the precise allegiance of particular patrons, whether individual or institutional. The issues seem more clearly defined, more purely religious and less political, in the seventeenth century, with artists such as Vouet, Poussin or Lebrun working for the Jesuits, Champaigne for the Jansenists at Port-Royal, and Lesueur evidently adapting his manner when he worked for the Carthusians at the Chartreux. But, Philippe de Champaigne also painted the high altarpiece for Saint-Louis, the most important Jesuit church in Paris, just as our 'Jansenist' Restout in the eighteenth century could equally work at Saint-Sulpice, where allegiances were strongly ultramontane [FIG. 3].

It is important to remember that painters were not theologians (although several religious orders had painters within their community, who worked for their churches), but in the first place were professional artists, who were pleased to respond to important commissions, especially in such public locations as churches. The known sympathies of a painter might to some extent determine what commissions most frequently came his way, and probably were a consideration of his patrons; however, in cases known to the present writer, patrons were more concerned about value for money than about the beliefs of the artist! Adaptability of manner to matter was

FIG. 3 J. Restout,
St Bruno Praying, Louvre

fundamental to the practice and the principles of the academic artist. Restout painted a wonderfully lyrical and even Correggio-like nocturnal *Nativity* (1760–1) in the Cathedral of Saint-Louis at Versailles, as a pendant to Pierre's great and tragic *Lamentation* (both pictures still *in situ*). For all that many of the church pictures have a high seriousness and grandeur of conception and execution, painters such as Restout, or the Coypels, Le Moyne, Van Loo, Pierre and Vien in this exhibition, could turn out charming profane and even gallant works when required.

Controversy is not obviously reflected in the religious works of the First Painters to the King, except in so far as their art remains orthodox and in line with a dominant tradition of imagery which extends back to the Counter-Reformation. As mentioned above, they all contributed to the schemes of decoration being undertaken in the more important Parisian churches. We have one direct connection with such a scheme, in Carle Van Loo's *Annunciation* (no. 14). This is the preparatory sketch for a painting which still decorates the east end of Saint-Sulpice, where it was originally placed in 1747 along with three companion pieces by Van Loo, and covered by Lemoyne's earlier painted dome. The original disposition of Van Loo's pictures was altered somewhat in 1774, when the architect Charles De Wailly splendidly refurbished their important chapel. Our sketch can stand for this kind of 'public' work undertaken by the First Painters, which it is inevitably not easy to represent in a gallery exhibition. Allowing for the spirited character of its execution as a sketch, the *Annunciation* also shows how the grand manner of seventeenth-century tradition was continued by religious painters throughout the eighteenth century.

While Charles Le Brun is best remembered for his cycles of ceiling decoration to the glory of Louis XIV at Versailles, it is less well known that he was also a moving religious painter, and was admired as such well into the eighteenth century. His altarpiece of *Christ Served by the Angels* (Louvre, Paris), originally painted for the church of the Carmelites in Paris in about 1653, is the prototype for his own pupil Antoine Coypel's treatment of the subject (no. 4). It also inspired two versions of the theme by Charles de la Fosse during the first decade of the new century (Private Collection, New York, and Musée des Beaux-Arts, Grenoble). In the last decade of his own life, Le Brun painted a suite of deeply-felt scenes from the life of Christ (Louvre, Paris, and museums at Troyes and Saint-Etienne), partly in rivalry with Pierre Mignard, who was deliberately (and ultimately successfully) challenging his position as Louis XIV's favorite. In a sense, they are also Le Brun's 'answer' to Poussin's celebrated *Seven Sacraments* of the mid-seventeenth century. The passionate religious emotion conveyed by these works of Le Brun is also captured in his smaller *Christ in the Garden of Olives* (no. 2), which owes something to Poussin in its clarity of design. Such a work expresses not only the deep devotion of its author, but also conforms to the pietistic enthusiasm of Louis XIV in the later decades of his life.

A classicizing and academically exemplary manner was continued throughout the early eighteenth century in religious works, and particularly those done for churches. But the lightness and elegance of the Rococo style (as it was to be dubbed much later) did also affect religious art. Even quite 'serious' works by Jean Restout or Charles-Antoine Coypel take on a certain mannered grace in the 1750's, not to speak of Boucher's always elegant and decorative art. For private collectors, risqué Biblical subjects such as *Lot and his Daughters* or *Susanna and the Elders* had been quite popular throughout Catholic Europe since the sixteenth century, and eighteenth-century France was no exception. Such religious subjects were but a pretext (and here lay some of the 'wit' in their selection) to show young and pretty female models in various states of undress, gazed upon by relatively elderly men, who within the picture act as surrogate spectators, mirroring the voyeuristic role of the actual owner of the painting.

Le Moyne's painting known as *The Amorous Proposal* (no. 9) is just this type of picture, handled with a luscious, but light and delicate touch, designed with the curling rhythms of the picturesque Rococo style, and sufficiently displaying the charms of a pretty girl to arouse our erotic interest. This painting is remarkably close to the Old Testament subject of Eliezer and Rebecca, when Eliezer chooses her at a well as a potential bride for Isaac. Strictly speaking, Rebecca should be drawing water, rather than washing clothes. Perhaps Le Moyne was simply making a personal variation on the theme, for the eighteenth-century spectator would certainly have identified the old man's garb as Biblical in kind.

Painted exactly ten years after the death of Le Moyne, Charles-Antoine Coypel's *St Piamun with her Mother* (no. 11) could hardly be more different in theme and mood. It is done with all the sobriety of one of Chardin's domestic interior scenes of these years, which often show the daily round of contemporary women and children, and embody moralizing meanings. However, the sparseness of the setting and the design and the attention to details such as the chipped stone wall, the bare floor-boards, and the elements of still life, show the influence of the more austere religious works of Restout and even Jouvenet. Piamun was an Egyptian girl referred to by the late fourth-century Christian commentator Palladius. He wrote about the spread of Christianity into Egypt, and was especially interested in the role there of holy women and mothers, who channelled their passions into austere forms of Christian devotion. No less than with Chardin, then, Coypel's painting (which must have been done for a patron with some antiquarian interest in early Christianity) makes a statement about the role of women, albeit in a religious rather than a secular context. But both artists seem to encourage women in their domestic tasks of spinning, reading and simple household economy, sheltered from the blandishments and the moral hazards of the world outside.

Coypel was unusual among the First Painters in not having made a trip to study in Italy, which was almost obligatory in the eighteenth century for the serious-minded history painter, as he worked his way through the academic system. In writing his biography of Jean Restout, who, as we have seen, did not travel to Italy either, the great critic and collector Jean-Pierre Mariette made a long parenthetical observation on the necessity of such a tour, if a painter was going to understand fully the academic Grand Manner.[12] In the present exhibition, the religious works of Le Brun, Antoine Coypel, Van Loo and Vien show the influence of Italian art. Van Loo's *Noli Me Tangere* (no. 13), painted in the year of his return from a seven-year tour of study south of the Alps, blends something of the discreet erotic charge of Correggio's treatment of this theme with the precise drawing and assured but delicate flesh-painting of Guido Reni. Vien's *St Theresa* (no. 20) of 1756 was executed during a period of stylistic transition in his art, when, largely under the influence of the antiquarian and theorist Comte de Caylus, he was moving away from a contrasted and painterly Baroque manner (influenced by Guercino and early Reni) towards the tighter, dryer and more classical approach for which he is conventionally better remembered. *St Theresa*, appropriately for such an exemplary Counter-Reformation scene of ecstasy, is still painted in his earlier manner, which he absorbed as a student in Rome during the later 1740's, and which has only recently been appreciated again for its own sensuous beauty. Indeed, for all that the Comte de Caylus saucily claimed to see in this image the likeness of a particularly attractive Carmelite sister, who allegedly sat for Vien,[13] the features of his *St Theresa* are surely rather based on an artistic model (not without its own irony), namely Guido Reni's *Magdalen* (National Gallery, London), a greatly admired work in the Orléans Gallery during the eighteenth century.

Vien's later, Neo-classical style is represented in this exhibition, not by a religious work, but by his *Venus Wounded by Diomedes* (no. 21), shown at the Salon of 1775. However, it is appropriate to mention here that at the same Salon he did show an important religious work, painted for the main altar of the Royal Chapel at the Petit Trianon, Versailles. When the work was commissioned in 1767 (its execution was delayed for various reasons), Louis XV took a personal interest in the selection of its subject. It shows the thirteenth-century St Thibault offering a basket of flowers to the first King Louis and Queen Marguerite of Provence, whereupon eleven lilies miraculously sprout into bloom, indicating the flourishing future of the Bourbon line. Thus religious painting was neatly and directly put at the service of the king, in an attractive and flattering confirmation of the House of Bourbon in France. The simple lines and shallow space of Vien's design perfectly complement the classical restraint of the architecture of Ange-Jacques Gabriel's chapel, where the painting is still to be seen today.

We cannot generalize about the Royal taste in religious painting, except that almost by definition it avoided controversy, and betrays a certain ultramontane sympathy. Louis XIV was influenced by Jesuit thought: and although for political expediency Louis XV presided over the expulsion of the Order from France, in private he too expressed sympathy for their cause.[14] The major religious works done specifically for the Crown in the eighteenth century must be Antoine Coypel's magnificent decoration (1707–10) of the Royal Chapel at Versailles, and the collective scheme of decoration (which took many decades to bring to completion) of Saint-Louis-des-Invalides in Paris, which included the First Painters Louis de Boullongne and Carle Van Loo among the successive teams of artists. Without enumerating yet more works here, we can see in the present exhibition that the First Painters all produced religious works when occasion demanded. As we would expect of artists with such distinguished academic careers, they readily adapted their manner to the specific demands of the subject and, where we can ascertain it, to the context of the commission in hand.

In the 1760's, notably after the expulsion from France of the Jesuits, religious controversy shifted more to the Enlightenment attack on the institution and the values of the Church; that is, the attack from the *philosophes* and *savants* to whom Horace Walpole refers in his letter cited at the beginning of this essay. Of course these thinkers and propagandists of reason had been intensely interested in seeing the destruction of Jesuit 'fanaticism'. The great minds that provided the intellectual thrust of the 'Age of Reason' were not particularly concerned to discuss contemporary religious imagery, but rather to attack what they perceived as the mystification of the religion itself, the manipulative power over men's minds and lives of the whole Christian ethos, and its manifestation in an often corrupt church hierarchy. This, of course, is not the place to discuss the rights and wrongs of this complex issue, but in justice it has to be said that the magnificence of the churches, the beauty and persuasive power of their painted imagery, did gloss over some brutal realities of religious life.

Perhaps the most famous 'cause' of the Enlightenment against the Church (a cause led by Voltaire) concerned the Catholic extremism of the Parlement of Toulouse in 1762, which out of religious bigotry condemned and executed the Protestant Jean Calas for the supposed murder of his son. Such were the national and international repercussions, that eventually Louis XV annulled the verdict of the parlement, and pronounced the innocence of the Calas family. The *philosophes* justly saw this as a significant moral victory for enlightenment over Catholic reaction. Another outcry arose in 1765, when a young nobleman of Abbeville was accused with others of defacing a wayside crucifix, and other blasphemous acts. They were also accused of the crime of reading Voltaire's recent *Dictionnaire Philosophique* and other banned and impious books. The young La Barre was condemned, horribly mutilated, beheaded, and his remains burned along with the offending literature. These are the most sensational cases and causes perhaps, but they serve to show that the issues at stake were not just a matter of detached intellectual debate.

One of the most celebrated and vocal of the *philosophes* was Denis Diderot (1713–84), editor from 1751 of the *Encyclopédie*, the great dictionary of Enlightenment thought, which not surprisingly was repeatedly banned and censured by the Crown and the Church, not least for its anti-clerical stance and its encouragement of incredulity. No discussion of French art in the second half of the century would be complete without invoking Diderot's name. He developed a lively interest in contemporary art through the critical reviews of the Salon exhibitions he wrote for the intellectual periodical the *Correspondence Littéraire* from 1759 to 1781. He investigated contemporary art and artists as thoroughly as any topic he might have written up for his *Encyclopédie*, and this activity brought him into contact with the religious painting of the day.

As a *philosophe* and atheist, however, it is not surprising to find that Diderot shows very little interest in religious painting as such. But he did at least put his own prejudices on one side to a certain extent, and gave plenty of space in his reviews to discussions of these prominent works at the Salons. Thus he fulfilled the descriptive and critical task his elite international readership expected, but by discussing religious works as history paintings, along with any other works based on mythological, literary or historical sources; and indeed he referred to Christianity as 'our mythology'. If the morality of a particular religious story held no interest for Diderot, it was still the legitimate task of the critic to discuss the effectiveness with which a painter presented it, how far through his imagination and his technical ability he had expressed appropriately a given subject. Thus Diderot was always prepared to give credit where he felt it was due. He also developed a good knowledge of the Old Masters he could study at first hand in Paris or through engravings, in order to sharpen his artistic judgment and to be in a position to make appropriate critical comparisons. Like his contemporary Horace Walpole, he was, for example, a great admirer of Lesueur's *Life of St Bruno* paintings at the Chartreux, although any consolation Diderot drew from them was aesthetic rather than Christian.

In narrative painting Diderot was especially drawn to subject matter of extreme dramatic interest, highly charged emotion, or the 'Sublime' in the eighteenth-century sense. He was delighted to find that the Bible and the martyrology of the saints could provide painters with ample scope for an art of this character. Just as ancient mythology in its loves of the gods provided the best subject matter of an agreeable sort, argued Diderot, so 'our mythology' abounded in 'crimes' worthy of truly tragic treatment. In Diderot's view as a man committed to the 'Age of Reason', Christianity throughout its history was responsible for more suffering than solace, for wars more than for peace, for agonies that were not redeemed by ecstasy. Thus in his early *Salon of 1763*, and with the cries of Calas still ringing in his ears, Diderot stated his own ideological position, while at the same time he extolled the veritable 'theater of cruelty' provided by the Christian religion for modern art:

> The blood which the abominable Cross has caused to flow on all sides is quite another resource for the tragic brush. . . . The crimes which the folly of Christ has committed and caused to be committed are so many great dramas, and of quite another order of difficulty, than the descent of Orpheus into Hell, the charms of Elysium, the punishment of Tenes, or the delights of Paphos. . . .

> Never was a religion as rich in crimes as Christianity; from the death of Abel to the punishment of Calas, not a line of its history is without bloodstains. What a beautiful thing is crime, in history and in poetry, on canvas and in marble.[15]

With his impassioned words, Diderot seems to take us forwards in time from the 1760's, when he was writing, beyond the Revolution of 1789, which put an end to First Painters to the King, and to anticipate the pure sensationalism of much Romantic art.

Notes

[1] *Horace Walpole's Correspondence*, ed. W. S. Lewis, vol. 14, 1948, pp. 144–5.

[2] C. A. Coypel, *Vies des Premiers Peintres du Roi*, vol. 2, 1752, p. 17.

[3] J. Crasset, *La véritable dévotion envers la S. Vierge établie et défendue*, 1679, pp. 110–11.

[4] L. Galloche (?), *Explication du tableau présenté à la Sainte Vierge . . . le premier jour de May 1705*, 1705, pp. 1, 3.

[5] C. A. Coypel, *Lettre de M. Ch. Coypel . . . au sujet d'un tableau*, 1729, p. 2.

[6] R. de Piles, *Cours de peinture par principes*, 1767 ed., p. 57.

[7] Abbé du Bos, *Réflexions critiques sur la poésie et sur la peinture*, vol. 1, 1770 ed., p. 216.

[8] L. S. Mercier, *Tableau de Paris*, vol. 4, 1782, p. 461.

[9] J. A. Piganiol de la Force, *Description de Paris*, etc., vol. 3, 1765 ed, pp. 459, 461.

[10] The best history of Jansenism is A. Gazier, *Histoire générale du mouvement janséniste*, 2 vols., 1924; see also D. Van Kley, *The Jansenists and the expulsion of the Jesuits from France*, New Haven, 1975, and R. R. Palmer, *Catholics and unbelievers in eighteenth-century France*, New York, 1939. On religious painting see P. Marcel, *La peinture française au début du dix-huitième siècle*, 1906; P. Conisbee, *Painting in eighteenth-century France*, Ithaca, 1981; A. Schnapper, *Jean Jouvenet*, 1974; P. Rosenberg and A. Schnapper, *Jean Restout*, catalogue of an exhibition at the Musée des Beaux-Arts, Rouen, 1970.

[11] L. B. Carré de Montgeron, *La vérité des miracles opérés à l'intercession de M. de Pâris*, 1737.

[12] *Abecedario de P. J. Mariette*, ed. P. de Chennevières and A. de Montaiglon, vol. 4, 1857–8, p. 384 (*Archives de l'art français*, vol. 8).

[13] F. Aubert, 'Joseph Marie Vien', *Gazette des Beaux-Arts*, 1867 (II), p. 180.

[14] Van Kley, *op. cit.*, p. 207.

[15] *Diderot: Salons*, ed. J. Seznec and J. Adhémar, vol. 1, Oxford, 1957, p. 214.

Some reflections on Boucher's early development

by Professor Jean-Luc Bordeaux

The eighteenth-century fear of boredom and search for happiness were partly responsible for the immense popularity of the female nude in the visual arts. In painting, women became objects of a form of love that equalled pleasure and desire without romantic involvement. The *cabinets*, bedrooms and boudoirs of the new Parisian *hôtels*, owned by those who held power through control of the nation's finances, were decorated accordingly, evoking a dream world where *joie de vivre*, elegance and seduction were transformed into a social function. Art then served a specific purpose: to move men to social action, with their search for happiness taking the fashionable form of the female nude. At no other time since Antiquity had the female nude become such a popular pictorial theme. The two principal artists who helped formulate the aesthetics of this new taste were François Le Moyne and François Boucher, both First Painters of the King.

It was during the 1720's that Le Moyne developed his ideal of female nudity which began with a spectacular *Andromeda* executed in 1723 (Wallace Collection, London), to be followed one year later by the sensual *Hercules and Omphale* (Louvre, Paris; and the beautiful autograph version exhibited here [no. 8]), and the elegantly modelled and attractive *Bather* known only from the extant autograph version exhibited in the Salon of 1725 (Hermitage, Leningrad). Le Moyne's feminine ideal was then composite and variable, either reminiscent of the sinuous fullness of Veronese and Rubens, the elongation of the body dear to the Italian mannerists working in Fontainebleau, or the soft contours and mellowness of Correggio's nudes. In the above works, Le Moyne established a type of feminine beauty that may not have caught the fancy of Hermann Voss or Sir Kenneth Clark but undoubtedly influenced his contemporaries such as Jean-Baptiste Van Loo and Noel-Nicolas Coypel and, more importantly, his own pupils, Boucher and Natoire and, indirectly, Pierre. *Andromeda's* voluptuous and generous forms, curved rhythms and glowing flesh tints had no parallel at that time in French art. Critics have often seen in Charles de la Fosse's and Antoine Coypel's earlier nudes an anticipation of Le Moyne's formal types. Louis de Boullongne's famous *Diana Resting*, executed in 1707 for the Chateau of Rambouillet (now in Tours), has also been seen as an eventual source of inspiration for the later success of bathing themes throughout the eighteenth century. However, Boullongne's picture may be much more relevant to the kind of academic sensuality expressed by the early nudes of Jean-François De Troy (Cleveland Museum of Art and J. Paul Getty Museum, Malibu) than to Watteau's *Diana Bathing* (Louvre, Paris) and Le Moyne's *Diana and Callisto* (A. Wengraf, London).

In the mid-1720's, Le Moyne's early eclecticism and monumental nudes yielded to a new ideal of naked beauty, smaller, more manageable and more intimately seductive, closer to the spirit of Watteau's nudes, illustrated by *Aurora and Cephalus*, painted in 1724 for the Hôtel du Grand Maître at Versailles, and by a series of enchanting *cabinet* pictures such as *The Abduction of Europa*, exhibited at the 1725 Salon [FIG. 1] (Pushkin Museum, Moscow), the *Diana and Callisto* of 1727, mentioned above, and *Venus and Adonis*, painted in 1729 (Nationalmuseum, Stockholm). These canvases are the direct forebears of Boucher's gallant mythologies executed after the latter's return from Italy. Ironically the influence of Le Moyne on Boucher, particularly noticeable in the 1720's, increased throughout the 1730's. Boucher's reception piece of 1734, *Rinaldo and Armida* [FIG. 2] (Louvre, Paris), the large pendants from the Watelet collection, *Venus and Vulcan* of 1732 [FIG. 3] (Louvre, Paris) and the Nancy *Venus and Adonis*

FIG. 1 Engraving by Laurent Cars after Le Moyne, *The Abduction of Europa*

FIG. 2 Boucher, *Rinaldo and Armida*, Louvre

FIG. 3 Boucher, *Venus and Vulcan*, Louvre

FIG. 4 Boucher, *Hercules and Omphale*,
Pushkin Museum, Moscow

FIG. 5 Boucher, *Mercury and the Infant Bacchus*, Wallace Collection, London

of the following year, the erotic *Hercules and Omphale* [FIG. 4] (Pushkin
Museum, Moscow) and the splendid and more elaborate compositions
from the Wallace Collection, *The Rape of Europa* and *Mercury and the
Infant Bacchus* [FIG. 5], represent Boucher's foremost tributes to a master
whose artistic debt he persistently refused to acknowledge. What is surprising is that, since the publication in the early 1950's of Hermann Voss'
important studies of Boucher's early development, more recent critics
have continued to ignore the evidence. Boucher's contemporaries, however, such as Mariette and Gersaint, never doubted Le Moyne's influence
on Boucher, while neither did the Goncourts, Paul Mantz, André Michel
and Pierre de Nolhac, who more than a century later wrote some of the
most enlightened pages on Madame de Pompadour's protegé.

François Boucher was born on September 15th 1703, the son of a minor
ornamentalist. His formative years continue to remain an enigma, but he

FIG. 6 Boucher, *St Bartholomew*,
Location Unknown

FIG. 7 Boucher, *Rebecca Receiving Gifts
Sent by Abraham*, Louvre

managed to be noticed in 1720 by Le Moyne, who praised his earliest recorded work, a lost *Judgement of Susanna*. This was probably a canvas Boucher presented to Le Moyne for his approval before being accepted in his studio, a common practice. Le Moyne had just been received by the Academy two years before with a *Hercules and Cacus* (École des Beaux-Arts, Paris). According to Mariette in his *Abecedario*, Boucher told this famous collector-connoisseur in 1767 (thirty years after Le Moyne's suicide) that he spent only three months with his master, who was a poor teacher. After Boucher's death, Mariette, feeling that the once popular artist had been deliberately forgetful and had repudiated Le Moyne's teaching out of vanity, commented ironically 'but then whose disciple was Boucher?'. In the absence of sufficient documentary evidence, one can only conjecture about the true reasons forcing the young artist to leave Le Moyne at such short notice. Mariette in his unpublished '*notes manuscrites*' (Cabinet des Estampes, Bibliothèque Nationale, Paris), and, above all, Marcel Roux (1934, Inventaire des Fonds Français, Cabinet des Estampes, Bibliothèque Nationale, Paris) seem to suggest that the real reason may not be unrelated to Boucher's lack of sufficient financial resources which prevented him from continuing his apprenticeship – a humiliation he most likely resented until the end of his life!

Boucher was then forced to accept a position as a designer in an engraver's workshop, that of Jean-François Cars, who, in the first place, might have advised Boucher to study under Le Moyne, since his own son, Laurent Cars, was at that time taking drawing lessons with him. During Le Moyne's lifetime, Laurent Cars engraved his master's most famous compositions. Shortly after this episode, Boucher produced a series of twenty-six drawings which were engraved in Cars' workshop to illustrate Gabriel Daniel's *Histoire de France*, published in 1722. These drawings, which had once belonged to Mariette, found their way into the Louvre with a new attribution. It was John E. Ruch who in 1964 reattributed these earliest traceable products of Boucher's hand which remind us of the seventeenth-century compositional schemes invented by François Perrier, Jacques Callot and Charles Le Brun. Boucher's career as a professional artist would take a major turn when Julienne offered him, in 1722, the opportunity to engrave Watteau's *Figures de Différents Caractères* and begin work on the famed *Recueil*. It remains difficult to judge what direct effect Watteau had on Boucher at this time, especially when one examines two small paintings on panel (*St Bartholomew* and *St Andrew* [FIG. 6]), recently rediscovered, which were part of a series of sixteen religious works engraved in 1726 by Jeurat, Aubert, etc (Cf. Ananoff, 1976, vol. I, nos. 12–27). These two pictures were reproduced for the first time by Pierre Rosenberg in the exhibition catalogue of the *Donation Kaufmann et Schlagter* (Louvre, Paris, 1984, p. 33). In the same catalogue Rosenberg reproduced two additional religious paintings from the same period, *Noah Offering a Sacrifice* and *Noah Leading the Animals into the Ark* (Private Collection, Fort Worth, Texas), which share similar stylistic characteristics with *Joseph and Jacob Before the Pharoah* (formerly and erroneously identified as Boucher's 1723 Prix de Rome *Evilmerodach Freeing Joachim* [Columbia Museum of Art, Columbia]); the small oil sketch in the Louvre representing *Rebecca Receiving Gifts Sent by Abraham* [FIG. 7], which is most likely to be a first idea for a painting sold at the Hotel Drouot (June 15th 1985) and engraved by Perronneau (Ananoff, 1976, vol. I, no. 33, though the format of the engraving does not correspond to that of either the sketch or the Drouot picture); the brilliantly coloured and richly contrasted *Sacrifice of Gedeon* recently acquired by the Louvre (*Kaufmann Donation*, op. cit., cat. no. 1); and a *Dream of Joseph* featuring a spectacular angel in the middle of the composition (Private Collection).

All these works and several others, like the lost *Meeting of Jacob and Rachel* and *The Departure of Jacob* (Ananoff, 1976, nos. 32 and 34), are not only religious subjects (Boucher's unexpected thematic preference during the

FIG. 8 Le Moyne,
*Nativity with the Adoration of
the Shepherds*, Novalessa, Italy

1720's) but they also reflect the young artist's undocumented admiration for the works of contemporary Venetian painters such as Pellegrini, Sebastiano Ricci (cf. Jeffery Daniels' *Sebastiano Ricci*, 1976, figs. 277–8) and, indirectly, Giovanni-Battista Tiepolo. Once more Le Moyne may have been the link between Venice and Boucher, since Pellegrini was the former's rival during the famous affair of the Banque Royale in 1720 and Le Moyne met Ricci in Venice during his visit there in 1724. Should all these religious works belong to the years Boucher spent in Italy; that is, from his arrival in 1728 to his return to Paris in 1731? Or could he have absorbed the style of contemporary Venetian painting in Paris or nearby London? The *Rebecca* oil sketch came to the Louvre with an attribution to Pellegrini and the beautiful angels and richly contrasted colour schemes of the *Sacrifice of Gedeon* and the *Dream of Joseph* may bring to mind an early work by Tiepolo, the *Vision of Saint Jerome* (formerly Cailleux Collection, Paris). However, the closer one examines these paintings, the more complex the chronology of Boucher's early work becomes. His early development continues to be problematic as the religious canvases executed in Italy may not be very different from those done prior to 1728.

There exists striking analogies regarding compositional arrangement, attitudes and gestures of figures between Boucher's religious works listed above and Le Moyne's *Jacob and Rachel*, painted in 1720 (replica with the Pardo Gallery, Paris), *Nativity with the Adoration of Shepherds*, painted in 1721 [FIG. 8] (formerly in the Church of Saint-Roch, Paris, now in Novalesa, near Susa, Northern Italy), or *Laban Seeking his Idols* [FIG. 9] (Musée des Beaux-Arts, Angers). In fact this kinship with Le Moyne was often pointed out in eighteenth-century sale catalogues (cf. Ananoff, 1976, cat. nos. 34–5). The combined influence of Le Moyne and Ricci may also be felt in gallant and pastoral subjects such as the nostalgically interpreted *Birth of Adonis* and *Death of Adonis*, certainly executed in Italy (Ananoff, 1976, cat. nos. 38–9). The elongated formal type of female figure portrayed in these pictures resembles that of Ricci during the 1720's (cf. Daniels, op. cit., figs. 70, 96, 156 and 208). When one compares Boucher's little known *Pastoral* [FIG. 10] (Musée des Beaux-Arts, Valenciennes), first rediscovered by Voss but ignored by Ananoff, to later landscapes executed in Italy or shortly after, such as *The Farm*, *Woman near a Fountain* and *Pastoral with a Fountain* (Ananoff, 1976, cat. nos. 42, 46 and 51), one must again question how much Boucher learned from his master in a genre to which Le Moyne until now was believed to have contributed little. However, the collection of the Prince de Conti included outstanding landscapes by Le Moyne which fetched high prices in eighteenth-century sales. Both artists' interpretations of nature was in essence italianate (cf. Locatelli, Zuccarelli and Zais), but their sensibility to nature reveals mysterious and deeper bonds than expected when Le Moyne's *Gallant Fishing Scene* [FIG. 11] (Private Collection) is compared to Boucher's Valenciennes *Pastoral*. I would date this latter work on the basis of the comparison with Le Moyne in the mid 1720's.

With Boucher's return to Paris in the summer months of 1731, his public career began. He was *agréé* in November of that year and was received by the Academy in 1734 with a charming canvas entitled *Rinaldo and Armida*. Interestingly, it was during the 1730's that Boucher seemed to have abandoned – for a while – the goal of achieving the coveted status of *peintre d'histoire sacrée*. Boucher's early models had been the masters of the baroque and several of his compositional drawings made in Italy (cf. Regina Shoolman Slatkin, *François Boucher in North American Collections: 100 drawings*, National Gallery of Art, Washington, 1973–4) reflected the seriousness of his purpose. However, the taste of the day in Paris had in the meantime completely turned to frivolity, therefore explaining the marvellous series of playful, sensual and gallant paintings starting with the Louvre *Venus and Vulcan*, the Nancy *Venus and Adonis* of 1733, the Pushkin *Hercules and Omphale*, the small canvases featuring sporting

FIG. 9 Le Moyne, *Laban Seeking his Idols*, Musée des Beaux-Arts, Angers

FIG. 10 Boucher, *Pastoral*, Musée des Beaux-Arts, Valenciennes

FIG. 11 Le Moyne, *Gallant Fishing Scene*, Private Collection

35

FIG. 12 Le Moyne, *Allegory of Drawing*, Pushkin Museum, Moscow

FIG. 13 Le Moyne, *Portrait of a Woman*, Location Unknown

children (Ananoff, 1976, cat. nos. 60–6) [also FIG. 12], the splendid *Rape of Europa* and *Mercury entrusting the young Bacchus to the Nymphs* from the Wallace Collection (to be dated respectively c., 1735–6 and 1737–8) and, of course, his reception piece, *Rinaldo and Armida*. All these works show that Boucher had acquired compositional maturity, coloristic brilliance and decorative originality on one hand and on the other had gone back unhesitatingly to the type of female nudity and sensuality made fashionable by Le Moyne a decade earlier in such works as the *Diana and Callisto* and the *Venus and Adonis*. The influence of Le Moyne can even be felt in Boucher's painting entitled *Woman with a Cat* [see page 31, fig. 1] (New Orleans Museum of Art), described in the sale catalogue of the Duke of Zweibrucken as 'tient beaucoup de la manière de François Le Moyne'. Boucher had actually borrowed from Le Moyne the positioning of the little girl as it appears in the latter's lost portrait of an unidentified woman and her child [FIG. 13]. The influence of Le Moyne became less and less obvious in the second half of the 1730's, though still noticeable in his decorations for the Hôtel de Soubise. It was indeed in his tapestry designs for Beauvais that Boucher revealed his truest originality and decorative virtuosity. The lessons of Italy were not forgotten in his cartoons for the *Fêtes Italiennes* and *The History of Psyche*.

Archaeology and Enlightenment
The Comte de Caylus and French Neo-Classicism

by Professor Dr Thomas Gaehtgens
translated by Sheldon Cheek

The new orientation which took place in French art around the middle of the eighteenth century cannot be described simply as a change of style. On the contrary a socio-political process was involved which art history alone cannot sufficiently explain. It was entirely characteristic of this era of radical change that questions relating to art and society were dealt with beyond the customary limits of specialized discussion. There was a general consensus that some sort of common effort was required if cultural renovation was to take place.

Of course conflicts over the establishment of goals and the methods to be used in the promulgation of cultural ideas, which were responsible for the accompanying changes in society, were unavoidable. In the history of French Neo-classicism the work and influence of Anne-Claude-Philippe de Thubières, the Comte de Caylus (1692–1766), played a decisive role in this polemic. (He personifies the way in which archaeology and antiquarian scholarship, the common passions of eighteenth-century France, could be the source of heated controversies.) If his work was criticized by some of his contemporaries, he nevertheless greatly influenced the course of the pictorial arts in France.

The Comte de Caylus has at present still not received an adequate assessment as a personality, teacher, poet and art propagator.[1] Overshadowed by his more famous counterpart J. J. Winckelmann, archaeologists have come only hesitatingly and by degrees to a revision of their opinions about him.[2] Since, in the scholarly sense, the Germans were the founders of the disciplines of archaeology and art history, only in recent times, after an amplification of the methodical approach to these professions, has the work of the Frenchman been better understood. Moreover, his work actually seems, in a time dominated by the aesthetic of Winckelmann, to be quite modern.[3] The description, from this viewpoint, of his influence and a consideration of the arguments central to his work is valuable not only for historical reasons but is a direct stimulus to discussions of method being pursued today.

The Comte de Caylus faced bitter opposition in his lifetime. This intense criticism was directed against his teaching activity as an archaeologist as well as a collector and promoter of art. An especially virulent sample of the attacks which his contemporaries inflicted upon him, without reservation and to the point of personal defamation, is found in the following account of his character:

> I have scarcely known the type of person for whom I have had as much an aversion as he had for me. I have never taken the pains to consider how I offended him; but I know well what displeased me about him. It was the importance that he gave to his most frivolous qualities and the slightest of his talents; it was the value which he attached to his trifling studies and to his antique trinkets; it was the sort of domination that he had usurped from artists and which he abused, favoring the mediocre talents who made up his court and discouraging those who, prouder in their resolution, did not solicit his support. It was, finally, a very adroit and refined vanity, and a very hard and imperious pride, disguised under the uncultured and simple forms in which he knew how to envelop them. Docile and gracious with the people whom the artists depended on, he procured with the former an authority dreaded by the latter. He accosted learned men, making them compose reports on the trinkets which the junk shop dealers sold him; he made a magnificent publication of these trifles which he held to be antiques; he proposed prizes for Isis and Osiris in order to have the air of himself being

initiated into their mysteries; and with this mockery of erudition he in-truded himself into the Academies, knowing neither Greek nor Latin. He had said so much, had had so much said by his long-winded preachers that in architecture he was the restorer of the 'simple style', of 'simple forms', of the 'beautiful simple', that the ignorant believed him; and in his relations with the dilettantes he passed in Italy and in all of Europe as the inspirer of the Fine Arts. I therefore have for him that type of natural antipathy which true and simple men always have for charlatans.[4]

This opinion of Caylus is not only hardly flattering, it is, as Jean Seznec remarked, a condemnation. The author of the quote is Jean-François Marmontel (1723–99), who reproached Caylus not only for his ambition and arrogance, but also for his dubious character. And in the same breath he clearly condemned the scholarly work and the collecting activity of the count, whom he characterized as a charlatan. Still more bitter, dry and sarcastic, Diderot remarked, after the death of Caylus in 1766, that: 'Death has delivered us from the most merciless of amateurs.'[5]

It is the contribution of Seznec to have elucidated the origins of this condemnation of the Comte de Caylus. In his book *Diderot et l'Antiquité*, Seznec has referred to the strongly divided camps, especially in France, of the *Encyclopedistes* and the *Philosophes* on one hand and the *Erudits* and the *Archaeologues* on the other. Accordingly *raison* or 'imagination' were important for Diderot, d'Alembert, Voltaire, Marmontel, Rousseau and Grimm as guides for a true grasp of the antique, whose exemplary nature was not doubted and whose lessons were to be applied to the present. Their contempt was directed toward the *Erudits*, men who spent their entire lives collecting facts and filling their minds, instead of enlightening the spirit, as Gibbon, who sought to mediate between both sides, expressed it.[6] *Erudits*, *Antiquaires*, *Archaeologues* and the *Académie Royale des Inscriptions et des Belles Lettres* which represented them were not held in high esteem. They were characterised as hair-splitters who devoted themselves to unworthy objects from which no knowledge useful for mankind could be extracted.

J. Casaubon, B. de Montfaucon, J.-J. Barthélemy and Caylus were singled out for scorn and rebuke as charlatans. Montesquieu had exclaimed: 'You are all charlatans, *Messieurs les antiquaires*'.[7] Furthermore, Diderot, one of the most resolute champions of the camp of *Philosophes*, condemned in an essay the *anticomanie* of the archaeologists who honored antiquity only because it was old. He then proceded to isolate what in the works of the antique should be admired as useful for the present.

The Comte de Caylus represented on the other hand a completely different point of view. For him the true conception of antiquity was derived first of all from the knowledge of all that was preserved of the ancient heritage. His efforts were therefore directed toward the compilation of an inventory of surviving works without respect to 'high or low art'. The admiration and analysis also of antique utilitarian objects, independent of their artistic quality, must therefore be the task of the archaeologist. In the fifth volume of his principal work, the *Recueil des antiquités, egyptiennes, grecques, etrusques, romaines et gauloises*, he countered the misunderstandings and the unflinching attacks of the *Encyclopedistes*. He realized that they had an inadequate approach to the study of the antique. Until then it had not been in any way definitively explored and had been considered from only one side, which could easily seem trivial. He asserted that he would also make light of any study that consisted of nothing other than considerations of some old heads or torsos.[8] For him, on the other hand, the history of the art and civilization of the antique was possible only through order and classification. This point of view determined the collecting activity of the count. His comprehensive collection lacked the great master works which the princes boasted. From agents, mostly in Italy, he bought medals, carved stones, bronzes and all types of antique vessels, as well as vase fragments. These works, which the *Encyclopedistes* mocked, did not always reach France through legal means. Diderot wrote disdainfully to Grimm:

> This man is completely astonished that the Ancients had cauldrons, spoons, forks; in a word, that having the same needs as we have, they invented the same means of providing for them. Wouldn't he also be surprised that they had a mouth and a rear end?'[9]

Caylus certainly did not limit himself to Greek objects or those things held to be Greek. From the outset he included in his collections and his studies works from the Orient, Egypt, Asia Minor, the Etruscan culture and, continuing the work of Montfaucon, Gallo-Roman objects. In spite of strong criticism, caused not without some envy, there can be no doubt that the collection of antiquities of Count Caylus was entirely the result of the serious scholarly interests of its owner. He was completely unmindful of prestige and the accumulation of valuable things or even financial speculation. Hence it follows that he bequeathed the entire collection to the king so that in the future it could be studied and consulted as a more or less public possession. The principal parts of it are found today in the Cabinet des Medailles of the Bibliothèque Nationale and in the Louvre.[10]

It is significant regarding this bequest that the donation was made in three steps. After the count had inventoried his collection for the first time, described, dated and analysed each of the pieces, engraved the collection in prints and published it in a catalogue, it lost its personal interest for him. His scholarly interest was satisfied. He cleared his house and transferred his treasures to the king to make room for new acquisitions which he dealt with in the same way. Twice in this manner he sent the objects collected by him to the king's palace, and after his death the accumulation of his subsequently gathered holdings also devolved to the king.

In Caylus we are thus presented with a mid-eighteenth century collector who, as archaeologist and scholar, as he would be thought of today, considered the works brought together by him to be public possessions. Only a few years previously voices had been raised in France which called for the accessibility of the Royal painting collection so that the revival of art through the study of great models might be realized. In order to improve the taste of the public and the amateurs, which had been misled by Regency and Rococo painting, the opening of a gallery was called for, although for organizational reasons this demand could only be satisfied a decade later.[11]

The antiquities collection of the Comte de Caylus must be understood in connection with the art-political movements, which, interpreted in a still current, exemplary and effective fashion by Jean Seznec, foresaw a revival of art around the middle of the eighteenth century in the manner of the *Grand Siècle*. The enthusiasm for the Antique brought about by the newly made finds in Pompeii and Herculaneum was not a motivating factor but only one furthering element of the development of these restorative art politics. Antiquity, which during the Renaissance and the *Grand Siècle* had been considered a model for art, was both revived and dealt with in a new fashion by this development.[12]

In France, Caylus played a decisive role in this process. From the beginning he strove to draw lessons for the art and culture of the present from the study of ancient objects. Himself a draughtsman, an engraver and an influential member of the *Académie Royale de Peinture et de Sculpture* and the *Académie Royale des Inscriptions et des Belles-Lettres*, he sought to advance art in a number of papers and in the bestowal of prizes. In this sense his chief work, the *Recueil*, which appeared from 1752 in seven volumes, is not only a catalogue of his own collection; in this way it was made available to the public and artists were presented with examples of antique art to be emulated and used as models.

In the foreword to the first volume Caylus discussed very precise methods and goals which were bound up with his work. For him the study of monuments contained the possibility of increasing the knowledge of the Antique. Certainly for his time it was unusual to amplify the written sources in such a way or even more so to question them. He reproached earlier antiquarians who cited isolated ancient monuments only to confirm historical facts. Rebelling against this he stressed the need to compare objects with each other and in this manner to understand their use. He classified the preserved evidence of antique art and the applied arts, not as confirmation of the ancient authors, who all too often muddled things with selected examples, but as individual objects whose treatment required its own scholarly method. He felt that practical knowledge should be sought from the monuments rather than the out-of-hand acceptance of the written sources and that comparative methods be used which had the same importance for the archaeologist as observation and experiment had for the physical scientist. The investigation of diverse monuments, carefully compared, enabled their use to be reconstructed, Caylus realized, as the study of natural phenomena resulted in the discovery of their inner organization and principles.[13]

The comparison with the scientist showed Caylus to be a scholar of the Enlightenment, whose methods in the arts approached the quality and kind of methods used in the natural sciences. Caylus informed his readers that his work was chiefly intended for scholars. He also embraced the concept of the '*Homme de lettres*', as one who only sought in the monuments of antiquity confirmation of the validity of the written sources. In contrast to the arrogance with which his critics charged him, he frankly admitted that he occasionally encountered some problems which his training and methods did not allow him to deal with adequately. He therefore produced another method which he hoped would be accepted by his colleagues in the arts. It involved the extremely careful comparison of a monument as an example of individual expression as well as the taste of its time and place of origin.[14] With it, the archaeologist's task would be the perception of the development of taste in a region during various centuries through the comparison of objects. In this way it would then be possible to come closer to a history of the arts. Accordingly, each volume of the *Recueil* contains an overview of the path of development of the arts from Egypt and via Etruria to Greece, then to Rome, and finally, in the last volume, in the Gallo-Roman provinces.

He sought to judge the shards of a vase as precisely as the great works of 'high art', painting and sculpture; he analyzed these fragments with the same precision and also recorded them in engravings. They served him as prime examples of the influence of a generally diffused culture which was characterized by 'noble simplicity':

> For it should be acknowledged that when they present beautiful forms and precise work, they serve more than all the passages of authors to prove the good taste which reigned in a nation. If such people had made this noble simplicity radiate, elevating the spirit on vases destined for the most ordinary use, what care would they not have taken in fashioning more precious things![15]

A special interest of the archaeologist was the technical processes by which ancient objects were produced. Concerning the uses which these processes had for contemporary artists, he always stressed the refinements of the technical fabrication of such works. Caylus extended this interest to actual practice in his efforts to reconstruct ancient working methods, such as encaustic painting. He thus demonstrated his belief that antiquity was superior to the present in the technical as well as the artistic aspects of its art. The essential task of the present must therefore be the attainment of the cultural standard of the past. Caylus formulated his task principally for the work of artists, and he never lost sight of the pragmatic utilisation of his undertakings. For the very reason that little had been written until then concerning this aspect of art, he provided an essential reference point for artists. The study of ancient works and monuments could, he hoped, cause his contemporaries to feel the need to work with a precision which was lacking at that time, when only a superficial splendor was all too frequently found. In this way working methods which had been lost could be reconstructed.[16]

Caylus therefore stressed the benefits which archaeological study could bring to contemporary artists. He sought to draw conclusions from the results of his investigations which he could transmit to artists as suggestions.

His influence was manifold. We have already mentioned his attempted reconstruction of encaustic painting. Typically, he did more than merely record it in a treatise, co-written with a natural scientist, the medical specialist Majault. He went on to induce artists like Joseph-Marie Vien, Louis Lagrenée and Louis-Joseph Le Lorrain to paint pictures in this technique.[17] His *Memoires sur la Peinture à l'Encaustique et sur la Peinture à la cire*, published in 1755, was not so much a learned exposition as it was a technical manual. Illustrated with prints were the working methods by which the reconstructed painting techniques of antiquity could easily be executed.

Of greater importance, however, were the writings in which the Comte de Caylus introduced artists to new pictorial themes. In the *Nouveau Sujets de Peinture et de Sculpture* of 1755, the *Tableaux tires de l'Iliade, de l'Odyssee d'Homere et de l'Eneide de Vergile, avec des observations générales sur la costume*, of 1757, and the *Histoire d'Hercule le Thébain, tirée de différents auteurs, à laquelle on a joint la descriptioin des tableaux qu'elle peut fournir*, of 1758, he assisted artists with practical handbooks comprised not only of ancient authors' works but also of proposals of possible representations of them in painting or sculpture.[18]

He had also borne incensed criticism, especially on the part of Diderot, for his thematic proposals. Above all, however, the fundamental objections to his conception of the study of antiquity were provoked by the fifth volume of his *Recueils*, appearing in 1763, in which he refuted prevailing ideas. He both defended and defined his position as a collector of antiquities and formulated his theories of archaeology. His statements are a fundamental assertion of the importance of this profession and they seem to have been unjustly ignored thereafter.

Caylus defended himself against the arrogance of his critics who considered his interpretation of the legacy of antiquity as the result of a misguided concern with unworthy objects. He countered the 'high-flown intellectuality' of his adversaries with a knowledge of the basic principles of study. The importance of archaeology was still scarcely understood. His critics too easily supposed that he was concerned only with the outer form of very commonplace objects. He was convinced that archaeology could become a *véritable philosophie* and could give order to the *sagesse* of the amateur.

The conviction of Caylus' that archaeology was no mere leisure-time activity, but was even capable of contributing to 'philosophy', involved him in a struggle against the *Encyclopedists*, who meant to monopolize this domain for themselves. In his activity Caylus proceded under two points of view: *le physique* and *le morale*.[19] The range of work to be performed by archaeologists was for him far-reaching. He considered '*le physique*' to involve the study of the people and the lands which created a work or monument. The outer form, the style, technique, material and use of the objects fall in the category of physical investigation. It enabled the elucidation of the ways of life, customs and character of the people who evolved them. In such a way archaeology afforded both a necessary complement to and a commentary on the writings of the ancient authors.

Caylus, however, was not satisfied with the extension of knowledge alone. He felt that discoveries should be made fruitful for the present. Archaeology was to yield knowledge not only as a goal in itself, but also to serve society, to which it facilitated the application in practical terms of extensive experiences of the past. As a member of both Academies, Caylus had often enough engaged in the transmission of knowledge. At the end of his life he could write against his enemies, not entirely without irony: 'It is therefore agreeable to work in the hope of procuring for one's fellows [even] the most mediocre benefit, while such a great number of men die insolvent in this regard.'[20]

This would certainly seem a sufficiently insightful point of view, yet Caylus was not satisfied with these perceptions themselves. For him the archaeologist could even extend his thoughts into the sphere of moral concerns, since he was in a better position than any other to become acquainted with mankind throughout the course of history. Through the opportunity to compare monuments with the aid of the written sources, he was even able to judge their customs, their character, their ways of behaviour. He could evaluate their mistakes and weaknesses and could even learn and teach how to avoid them. And above all he was very soon to learn how slowly and in what a halting way the great discoveries of mankind are made:

> But the greatest object of meditation for the antiquarian, that which is the most closely linked to his research, will without doubt be the slowness and the mediocrity of the innovative genius which attribute to themselves...'.[21]

Caylus conceived of a concept of history in which the important discoveries of mankind were in no way ascribable to a few highly gifted people. It appeared to him much more likely that the accumulation of chance occurrences, which after long periods of time were transformed into discoveries, was characteristic of development in the history of mankind's progress. The archaeologist was, in his opinion, the most qualified to make this observation, since he alone could evaluate this development through the comparison of surviving objects.

Caylus cited as examples the discovery of the wheel or the use of fire, whose useful application was found by primitive cultures over a long period of development. This lengthy process seemed to Caylus to be one of the essential perceptions of the archaeologist. With this insight he found confirmation that the study of antiquity could also lead to intuitions of a moralistic sort concerning mankind. The archaeologist could follow the development of mankind as it awakened from its first centuries, found its gods and developed its superstitions and its fears into cults. For Caylus the antiquarian was an impartial judge, who witnessed the rise and fall of cultures and empires. He, the archaeologist, is in a position to observe the shortcomings and the vanities of peoples and is able to evaluate the contribution which they made to history. In this work the archaeologist observes few names; the anonymity of the historical continuum seems as characteristic to him as the appearance of a few great names and a few great works of art. He confirms, rather, the existence of 'millions of men, drowned in the abyss of time and carried away by the whirlwind'.[22] And the very transitoriness of the monuments causes the student of antiquity to reflect on the vanity of egotism, 'that great enemy of men' and the greatest and most calamitous nemesis of society. The study of antiquity is consequently a humanitarian concern, it is all-embracing. It offers the possibility to perceive, understand and also to exculpate the failings of mankind.

Caylus' 'Prologomena' to the profession of archaeology is no philosophical system, as Winckelmann set out in his history of the art of antiquity. For him, history, the evidence of which he studied, remained his foremost concern. He did not seek the basic principles of a systematic aesthetic.

FIG. 1 La Lorrain,
Writing table made for
La Live de Jully, 1757

When Herden remarked of Winckelmann in his *Kritischen Waldern* (Critical Forest): 'Winckelmann, a teacher of Greek art, is himself more mindful in his art history of producing a historical metaphysic of beauty drawn from the ancients, particularly the Greeks, than of history proper', he could in contrast have observed of Caylus that the highest goal for him was the tracing of the reality of history.[23] 'Historical tradition for him did not represent lifeless erudition', but was the source material for the proper renovation of the fundamentals of basic instruction.[24]

The profound effect of the work of Caylus is very clear in the development of culture during the second half of the century in France. His influence on the pictorial art in eighteenth-century France has still not been sufficiently studied. Besides encouraging painters to experiment with encaustic painting, the development of sculpture also concerned him. We know of his regard for the sculptor Edme Bouchardon, who in many respects he supported and promoted.[25] The effect of his writings in which he suggested pictorial themes to artists can only be more slowly evaluated.

Of special influence, however, were his studies and his collections in the realm of decoration and design. With Blondel, Laugier, Leblanc, Lafont de Saint-Yenne and others he found fault with the Rococo style and advocated instead a 'noble simplicity' of the 'Greek style'. He praised the furniture by La Lorrain for the apartment of La Live de Jully, whose writing table of 1757, one of the earliest examples of antiquising design, was probably produced from decorative forms furnished by Caylus.[26] [FIG. 1]

His efforts were directed toward the attainment of a renovation of pictorial art in France. The objects of his collection and his varied studies of ancient art and culture could thereby be a standard for this revival and provide guidance for artists. In his proposals he placed no value on heroic pictorial themes, but sought to resolutely advance the appreciation of Greek genre scenes which would embody 'noble simplicity'. The focus of his influence was directed toward the transformation of a culture based on evidence of Greek civilisation which had been rediscovered with the aid of archaeology.

The impression produced by the collections and studies of the Count of Caylus introduced a fashion *à la Grecque* in France. It involved a refinement of customs for which certain periods of Greek history and works from them were chosen as models. Himself a noble, Caylus stood therefore around the middle of the century among influential officials of the Royal court, such as the Marquis de Marigny and, later, the Count d'Angiviller, both Directors of Buildings of the king. The courtly society quickly adopted the new initiatives. Madame de Pompadour, Madame du Barry and Queen Marie-Antoinette were the outstanding protagonists of the

FIG. 2 J.-H. Fragonard,
The Lover Crowned,
Frick Collection, New York

FIG. 3 Vien, *La Jeune Athenienne*, 1762,
Private Collection

FIG. 4 Vien, *The Temple of Hymen*, 1773,
Préfecture de Chambéry, Savoie

'conversion' to the *goût Grecque* in the sense of a refined way of life in new guise. The Petit Trianon and its decor and Madame du Barry's chateau at Louveciennes, in which the Rococo scenes of Fragonard [FIG. 2] were replaced by 'antique scenes corrected from the Greek', are high points of the Greek mode.[27] [FIG. 3 and FIG. 4]

The courtly society rejected the Rococo style only in its outer form. Archaeological precision could become a scale of values in and of itself with nothing at all to do with the revival of a mode of life and the moral propositions that Caylus himself essentially had in mind.

The transformation of society on the order of the 'Greek' example consequently stiffened into a mere formula. And the *philosophes* and many artists of the younger generation could concern themselves, in the place of superficial stylistic change, with the representation of true virtues. With Diderot's highest praise, Greuze, to whom as a genre painter he ascribed the quality of a painter of history, was engaged at the same time in the challenge of raising bourgeois genre to the level of history painting. Bourgeois power, then in the process of freeing itself, chose before and during the Revolution chiefly Roman republican themes. It must have been aware of the contrasts between the Roman and the Greek cultures, since the 'pseudo-Greek way of life' had long since been identified with aristocratic society. The liberation of the Roman from the yoke of the Greek is an expression of the tension which the societal confrontation caused.

The Comte de Caylus died in 1766. He had not directly contributed to the polarization of the concepts of Greek and Roman culture. However, in France he had prepared through his work the basis and an example for the possible direct political effects which archaeology could produce. 'Art history represents a cultural enrichment of a particular sort which because of the vividness of its objects is especially intensive. With it one seizes the past through art, its immediate and most innate expression. And this has its value, because culture also signifies our belief that one comprehends the present from the basis of the critical understanding of the past', wrote Bianchi-Bandinelli in his *Introduzione all'archeologia*.[28] This conception is not far from that of the Comte de Caylus, even if Bandinelli did not have the eighteenth-century Frenchman in mind. Perhaps one could say with some caution that the 'modernity' of Caylus did not occur by chance just at the moment when the exclusively aesthetic consideration of important art works was pushed further in the background or when a comprehensive quest for the interpretive models of the phenomenon of culture was begun.

Notes

[1] The fullest, most thorough biographies are still: S. Rocheblave, *Essai sur la comte de Caylus, l'homme, l'artiste, l'antiquaire*, Paris, 1889; A. N. Zadoks-Josephus Jitta, *De Comte de Caylus als Archeoloog*, in *Tijdschrift for Geschiedenis*, 61, 1941, pp. 290–7.

[2] See in this regard W. Schiering, *Zur Geschichte der Archaeologie*, I. Von Bernard de Montfaucon zu Johann Joachim Winckelmann, in: *Allgemeine Grundlagen der Archaologie, Handbuch der Archaologie*, Munchen, 1969, p. 11 ff. See also: C. Justi, *Winckelmann und seine Zeitgenossen*, 5, Auflage, Koln, 1956, pp. 104–14. Also: F. J. Hausmann, *Eine vergessene Beruhmtheit des 18. Jahrhunderts: Der Graf Caylus, Gelehrter und Literat*, in: *Deutsche Vierteljahresschrift fur Literaturwissenschaft und Geistesgeschichte*, Jg. 53, 1979, Heft 2, pp. 191–209; J. Guillerme, *Caylus «technologue»; note sur les commencements problematiques d'une discipline*, in: *Revue de l'Art*, 60, 1983, pp. 47–50.

[3] 'And in the perspective of history, Caylus has not played a less important role than Winckelmann for the progress of classical archaeology in the eighteenth century. In fact, the work of Caylus, in its acuity and its concern with precise detail, is more closely related to modern science than the ambitious speculation of his German rival', judged J. Seznec, *Essais sur Diderot et l'antiquité*, Oxford, 1957, p. 95; see also N. Himmelmann, *Utopische Vergangenheit, Archaeologie und moderne Kultur*, Berlin, 1976, p. 53.

[4] Cited from J. Seznec, op. cit., p. 86.

[5] D. Diderot, *Salons*, edited by J. Seznec, vol. II, Oxford, 1979, p. 60.

[6] J. Seznec, op. cit., p. 82.

[7] Ibid, p. 85.

[8] The first volume of the *Recueil des antiquités egyptiennes, grecques, etrusques, romaines et gauloises* appeared in 1752. See also J. Seznec, op. cit., p. 88.

[9] Cited from J. Seznec, op. cit., p. 85.

[10] J. Babelon, *Choix de Bronzes de la Collection du Comte de Caylus*, Paris-Bruxelles, 1928.

[11] J. Locquin, *La peinture d'histoire en France de 1747 à 1785*, Paris, 1912; G. F. Koch, *Die Kunstausstellung*, Berlin, 1967.

[12] The account given by Jean Locquin, op. cit., offers the best overview to date. See also L. Hautecoeur, *Rome et la renaissance de l'antiquité à la fin du 18e siècle*, Paris, 1912. The catalogue is extremely informative: *Piranese et les français*, 1740–90, Académie de France à Rome, 1976.

[13] Caylus, *Recueil*, vol. I, p. III.

[14] 'It consists of the faithful study of the spirit and the hand of the artist, the cognisance of his views, of following them in execution, in a word, of the consideration of these monuments as the proof and the expression of the taste which rules in a [certain] century and in a [certain] place'. Ibid, p. VIII.

[15] Ibid, p. XI.

[16] Ibid, pp. XI–XII.

[17] Th. W. Gaehtgens, *Diderot und Vien, Ein Beitrag zu Diderots klassizistischer Asthetik*, in: *Zeitschrift fur Kunstgeschichte*, 36, 1973, 1, pp. 51–82.

[18] D. Wiebenson, *Subjects from Homer's Iliad in Neoclassical Art*, in: *Art Bulletin*, 46, 1964, pp. 23–37.

[19] J. Seznec, op. cit., p. 88.

[20] Caylus, *Recueil*, vol. I, p. VIII.

[21] Ibid.

[22] Ibid, p. XV.

[23] Cited from C. Justi, op. cit., vol. III, pp. 129–30.

[24] C. Justi, op. cit., vol. III, p. 131.

[25] Comte de Caylus, *Vies d'Artistes du XVIIIe Siècle, Discours sur la Peinture et la Sculpture*, edited by A. Fontaine, Paris, 1910, p. 76 (*Vie de Bouchardon*).

[26] S. Eriksen, *Early Neo-Classicism in France*, London, 1976, p. 46. pl. 85.

[27] J. Lugand, *De la folie de Louveciennes au chateau des ducs de Savoie*, in: *Revue de Savoie*, 1956, pp. 251–8; F. M. Bieber, *Fragonard and Madame Du Barry*, in; GBA, 102, vol. 56, 1960, p. 207, W. Sauerländer, in: *Uber die ursprungliche Reihenfolge von Fragonard's 'Amours des Bergers'*, in: *Munchner Jahrbuch der Bildenden Kunst*, Bd. 19, 1968, p. 127 ff; D. Posner, *The true path of Fragonard's «Progress of Love»*, in: *Burlington Magazine*, vol. 114, 1972, pp. 526–34.

[28] R. Bianchi-Bandinelli, *Klassische Archaologie. Eine kritische Einfuhrung*, Munchen, 1978, p. 167.

CATALOGUE

by Colin B. Bailey M.A.

Many people have helped make the task of writing these entries a great deal easier. The Service de Documentation of the Department of Paintings at the Louvre provided essential research material and the Photographic Service of the Musées Nationaux could not have been more helpful. Among the many individuals who answered questions and offered invaluable help with individual paintings I would like to thank Joseph Baillio, Richard Beresford, Sylvie Chambadal, Thomas Gaehtgens, Nicole Garnier, Pontus Grate, Michel Gregor, Christel Haffner, Monique Halbout, Francis Haskell, François Heim, Georges de Lastic, Thierry Lefrançois, Sylvain Laveissière, Marianne Roland Michel, Régis Michel, Messrs Pardo, Jacques Petithory, Marie-Catherine Sahut, Katy Scott and Alan Wintermute.

I owe special thanks to three people. To Alastair Laing, who passed on unpublished material to me with extraordinary generosity, and to my friends Anne and Udolpho van de Sandt, who read through my typescript with characteristic care and attention to detail for which I am especially grateful.

Colin B. Bailey

Abbreviations used in text:

B S H A F Bulletin de la Sociéte de l'Histoire de l'Art Français.

G B A Gazette des Beaux Arts.

Charles Le Brun
Paris 1619–1690 Paris

Le Brun was the first painter to hold the official title of First Painter of the King, and he remained until the end the ideal against which most subsequent First Painters were measured. Brilliant painter, master decorator, and tireless administrator, his rule over French artistic life was unprecedented. As a youth Le Brun entered the studio, first of Perrier, later of Vouet. He established his reputation and, in 1642, he followed Poussin to Rome, returning to Paris in 1646. Between 1647 and 1651 he completed his first large religious commissions for Notre-Dame, followed by his first decorative projects, for the Hôtel Lambert. He decorated Fouquet's Château of Vaux-le-Vicomte from 1658 to 1661, for which was probably painted *Venus Clipping Cupid's Wings* (Museo de Arte de Ponce). In 1664 he was granted the title *Premier Peintre du Roi* and subsequently served as Director of both the Academy and the Gobelins. Among his most renowned accomplishments for the King are the decoration of the Galerie d'Apollon in the Louvre and much of the interior of Versailles. He maintained his power and position under Louis XIV's patronage until the death of Colbert in 1683, when Louvois, Colbert's successor, shifted favor to Le Brun's great rival, Mignard. Until his death seven years later, Le Brun continued to refine his influential classical painting style through easel-sized religious paintings. The 1963 Versailles exhibition catalogue by Jacques Thuillier and Jennifer Montagu remains the best reference source.

Charles Le Brun

1 *Hercules Overcoming Diomedes*

Oil on canvas, H.23½in. W.16¾in.

Coll. Early provenance unknown; Private Collection, Paris.

Lent by a Private Collector, Paris.

Exhibitions: Versailles, 1963, *Charles Le Brun*, no. 3; London, Heim Gallery, *French Paintings and Sculptures of the Seventeenth Century*, Summer exhibition, 1968, no. 30.

FIG. 1 Le Brun,
Hercules Overcoming Diomedes,
Castle Museum, Nottingham

FIG. 2 Le Brun,
Hercules Overcoming Diomedes,
Pen and ink, black chalk,
Private Collection

This sketch of *Hercules Overcoming Diomedes* is probably the *bozetto* the young Le Brun presented to Cardinal Richelieu before executing a *dessus de cheminée* for the Palais Cardinal – the artist's first major Parisian commission.[1] The final work, which passed into the Orléans collection and is now in the Castle Museum, Nottingham [FIG. 1], is very close to the sketch but with important differences. The shoed hoof that appears below the neck of the horse on the left of the composition is positioned midway between the horse and Hercules in the sketch, yet is wedged tightly against the horse's neck in the finished picture. Similarly, this horse's left leg – crushed by the darker mare whose head sweeps into the center foreground of the composition – is almost tucked under the latter's jaw in the sketch, but is placed further back in the painting.

The drawing for this group of horses in the Bibliothèque Nationale repeats the arrangement of limbs followed in the final version of the picture, as, in fact, does a spirited preparatory drawing in far freer style and where the influence of Le Brun's first teacher, François Perrier, is manifest [FIG. 2].[2] In comparing this drawing with our sketch a second major difference appears in the positioning of Hercules' club, which hangs rather limply in the drawing and gradually rises through forty-five degrees in the sketch to an almost horizontal position in the final painting. It is remarkable that in all three works, Le Brun has achieved an energy and vigour that is not attenuated in the process of reaching the finished picture.

The violent scene represented is Hercules eighth labor: he was ordered to capture the four savage mares that Diomedes, King of Thrace, fed with the living flesh of his unsuspecting guests. Hercules is shown stunning Diomedes with his club while the horses strain at the opportunity to devour the body of their former master.

Although eighteenth-century commentators claimed that Le Brun painted this work at the age of fifteen, the *Hercules Overcoming Diomedes* has been dated slightly later, to between 1638–9 and 1641.[3] The painting was *in situ* by 1642 and elicited Poussin's warm approval. He is supposed to have remarked that,

> what he saw was either by a young man who would become one of the greatest painters that ever lived, or, if by someone older, this was an artist who could justly be called a talented man.[4]

Although Nivelon was full of admiration for Le Brun's 'manière nouvelle' in this *oeuvre de jeunesse*, historians have noted the influence of Perrier and Vouet in this vital and dynamic composition whose warm flesh tones and bravura modelling are Italianate in inspiration. In *facture*, composition and luminosity, *Hercules Overcoming Diomedes* is to be related to the larger altarpiece of the *Martyrdom of St John the Evangelist* (Church of Saint-Nicolas du Chardonnet, Paris), the last picture Le Brun would paint before accompanying Poussin to Rome in 1642.[5] Paradoxically, the young artist would shed this Italianate manner almost as soon as his protracted stay in Rome came to a close.

1 Charles Le Brun, *Hercules Overcoming Diomedes*

FIG. 3 J.-B.-M. Pierre,
Hercules and Diomedes,
Musée Fabre, Montpellier

Although the provenance of our sketch is yet to be established – Jacques Thuillier has connected this sketch to a painting of the same subject inventoried in 1699 among the effects of Le Brun's widow, Suzanne Butay – the final version was well-known during the eighteenth century. A drawing after the composition is to be found in the Louvre, Cabinet des Dessins (Inv. 27681), and a copy of our sketch is at the Musée d'Angers. Le Brun's painting provided the model for the *morceau de réception* of a later *Premier Peintre*, Jean-Baptiste-Marie Pierre, whose *Hercules and Diomedes* [FIG. 3] (Musée Fabre, Montpellier), painted a century later than Le Brun's, appears melodramatic and postured in comparison.

Notes

[1] This entry is based on the excellent entries in J. Thuillier and J. Montagu, *Charles Le Brun*, exhib. cat., Versailles, 1963, nos. 2 and 3.

[2] *Idem.*, no. 58. Le Brun's preparatory drawing is in a private collection, Paris.

[3] Thuillier and Montagu, *op. cit.*, no. 2, and A. Blunt, 'The early work of Charles Le Brun – 1', *Burlington Magazine*, August 1944, p. 166.

[4] Nivelon, quoted in Thuillier and Montagu, *op. cit.*, no. 2.

[5] *Ibid.*, no. 4.

Charles Le Brun

2 *Christ in the Garden of Olives*

Oil on canvas, diameter 54½in.

Coll. (?); 'Acheté au Sieur Paillet', March 1695; Versailles: Cabinet aux trois portiques, Versailles: Cabinet des Tableaux, 1706; Versailles: Hôtel de la Surintendance, 1760; Versailles: Magasins. 1, 1784; nineteenth-century provenance unknown; Private Collection, France; Stair Sainty Matthiesen.

In the late 1650's, Le Brun painted a series of religious pictures representing the *Mysteries of the Passion* and the *Lives of the Fathers in the Desert* for one of his most generous patrons, the Marquise Suzanne du Plessis-Bellière (1605/6–1705). This cultivated and well-connected woman, an intimate associate of Nicolas Fouquet – who provided a dowry of 200,000 livres for her daughter, the future Marquise de Créquy – had 'withdrawn from society' after the death of her husband in December 1654. The religious paintings that decorated her country house at Charenton presumably reflected this state of mourning. François Bellin was responsible for painting 'de très beaux paysages ... dans le bon goût de Fouquières' to which Le Brun added the figures of the Holy Fathers.[1] Le Brun further painted the Marquise's portrait as Artemis holding the ashes of her husband in an urn, and, according to Le Brun's pupil and biographer, Claude Nivelon, the artist 'lui fit présent d'un *Christ en prières au Jardin des Olives*'.[2]

This picture, a version of which we show here, presents considerable difficulties for the historian. At least two versions of the subject were known during Le Brun's lifetime. According to Le Brun's obituary notice in the *Mercure Galant* (February 1690), Fouquet had spoken to Cardinal Mazarin of Le Brun's paintings at Charenton and the Cardinal expressed interest in seeing his work:

> M. Le Brun then borrowed from Mme Duplessis-Bellière the painting of *Our Saviour in the Garden of Olives* which he showed the Cardinal. His Eminence hung this picture above his bed and told Le Brun that he was sure that Mme Duplessis-Bellière would agree to let it stay with him and would be satisfied with the copy Le Brun should make for her.[3]

Mazarin, in turn, was responsible for introducing Le Brun to Anne of Austria, the Queen Mother, and is said to have spoken so favorably of him that she too asked to see Le Brun's latest work. This time, Nivelon recounts the consequences:

> M. Le Brun, having nothing new or portable to show, had recourse to Mme Duplessis-Bellière who gave him the *Prayer in the Garden* from her *cabinet*, which was merely a work retouched by the artist (n'est même qu'une chose retouchée de lui).[4]

This must refer to the copy Mazarin had commissioned to replace the original *Christ in the Garden of Olives*. The second version remained in Anne of Austria's oratory and Le Brun was regally compensated with 'a golden chain of great value and a watch covered with diamonds.'[5]

If two versions of the subject can be documented to before 1660 the issue is compounded by the appearance in 1661 of Gilles Rousselet's engraving after Le Brun's *Christ in the Garden of Olives*, dedicated to the Marquise Duplessis-Bellière, the luckless owner of the painting.[6] Rousselet's engraving [FIG. 1] is not after our painting which differs from it in several important details. Quite apart from the different format, the sleeve of Christ's cloak falls across the lower arm of the supporting angel in the painting: in Rousselet's engraving the drapery does not break the line of the angel's left arm. There are no cherubim in Rousselet's engraving: the cloud of angels forms an important decorative motif in our painting. Finally, the consoling angel seems almost to stroke the neck of the fire-

FIG. 1 G. Rousselet, after Le Brun,
Christ in the Garden of Olives,
B. N. Cabinet des Estampes

53

blowing serpent in the engraving: in our painting his hand enters the serpent's jaw directly. In all likelihood the engraving is after the smaller tondo acquired by Catherine the Great and in the Hermitage, Leningrad.[7]

After all this it might seem reasonable to argue that our picture was not known by any of the seventeenth-century commentators that we have cited. However, it is absolutely certain that our *Christ in the Garden of Olives* – or a smaller version – was seen independently of the painting engraved by Rousselet. Claude Nivelon ended his lengthy description of 'le Christ au Jardin, gravé par M. Rousselet' with a discussion of the background. Behind the angel: 'the apostles, slightly in the distance and asleep, as it is written'. And in the far distance: 'those who were required to take possession of His person, who are seen entering the place'.[8]

In neither Rousselet's engraving, the Hermitage tondo, nor any of the subsequent or variant engravings, is this passage depicted in the background. Invariably we see a solitary tree and night about to fall. Our painting, by contrast, follows Nivelon's text to the letter. Judas signals to the soldiers who appear carrying torches and who are about to carry off the suffering Christ.

It is thus possible – but this remains hypothetical at present – that our painting is either the original *Christ in the Garden*, painted for Mme Duplessis-Bellière and commandeered by Mazarin – or a larger version of it – and that Rousselet's engraving is after the second version, retouched by Le Brun, and acquired by Anne of Austria. Guillet de Saint Georges noted that Le Brun had painted for her 'un *petit* tableau représentant le *Sauveur aux Prières*', which is unlikely to correspond to our large-scale work and may well describe the Hermitage tondo.[9]

Although a painting by Le Brun of Christ in the Garden of Olives was inventoried – by the artist himself – in Colbert's collection (1683), the absence of any indication of size or format makes it difficult to connect this picture with ours.[10] What does seem more certain, however, is that our painting entered the royal collection in 1695: a tondo of exactly the same dimensions was acquired by the *Bâtiments de Roi* from 'Sieur Paillet' in March of that year and is listed in various inventories for Versailles until 1784 when it was relegated to storage.[11] Le Brun's *Christ in the Garden of Olives*, was presumably sold off during the Revolution, but further research is needed to document our picture's history at the end of the eighteenth century.

The story of Christ's agony at Gethsemane is told in Luke 22, 39–48. Christ's acceptance of the chalice is symbolic of His sacrifice and salvation in accordance with God's will ('Father, if thou be willing, remove this cup from me. Nevertheless, not my will, but Thine be done'.). Le Brun follows the scriptures with graphic fidelity: Luke recounts that, being in agony, Christ prayed more earnestly, 'and his sweat was, as it were, great drops of blood falling down to the ground'. Indeed, we see trickles of blood on Christ's face, neck and arms. Yet the presence of a second angel holding the sacred chalice is not found in Luke. Nivelon interpreted this figure as confirmation of God's will and saw in the fire-breathing dragon a reference to original sin: 'that which brought about the downfall of the first Adam and for whose expiation Christ suffered death'.[12]

Even if Le Brun's sources are eclectic – he drew upon Vouet, Poussin and Sacchi for the large-eyed angels and suffering Christ – his coloring is at once daring and refined. The pinks of the cherubim's wings, the orange and purple robes of the consoling angel, as well as the red and green juxtaposition of those of the heavenly figure, are almost reminiscent of a Mannerist palette. Yet Le Brun's *Christ in the Garden of Olives* was perfectly suited for the urbane and sophisticated audience whose spiritual demands were satisfied by an imagery midway between Poussin's austerity and the full-blown Baroque Le Brun had encountered in Rome.[13]

2 Charles Le Brun, *Christ in the Garden of Olives*

Apart from the Hermitage tondo, several copies of the subject are known, notably a roundel painted after Rousselet's engraving, and so with the figures in reverse of our painting, in the Musée de Tessé, Le Mans. There is also a 'copie ancienne' in the Musée d'Angers.[14] Although no preparatory drawings for *Christ in the Garden of Olives* are known, a sheet of studies in the Cabinet des Dessins, Louvre (Inv. 27847) includes an angel in similar, but not identical, position to the chalice-bearing figure in our painting.

Notes

[1] H. Jouin, *Charles Le Brun et les arts sous Louis XIV*, Paris, 1889, pp. 130–2.

[2] Cl. Nivelon, *Vie de Charles Lebrun et description détaillée de ses ouvrages* (c. 1700), *Bibl. Nat., Manuscrits*, Fond Français, 12987, fol. 90.

[3] *Mercure Galant*, Fevrier 1690, p. 256.

[4] Nivelon, *op. cit.*, fol. 133.

[5] *Ibid.*, fol. 147.

[6] D. Wildenstein, 'Les oeuvres de Charles Le Brun d'après les gravures de son temps', *G.B.A.*, 66, (1965), p. 11, no. 62.

[7] The painting is reproduced in Anthony Blunt's magisterial article, 'The early work of Charles Le Brun', *Burlington Magazine*, August 1944, p. 189, plate 2.

[8] Nivelon, *op. cit.*, fol. 147, 'et dans le fond ceux qui furent commis pour se saisir de sa personne, qui entrent dans ce lieu'.

[9] Guillet de Saint-Georges, 'Mémoire historique des principaux ouvrages de Charles Le Brun', L. Dussieux, et al., eds., *Mémoires inédits sur la vie et les ouvrages des membres de l'Académie Royale de Peinture et de sculpture*, 2 vols, Paris, 1854, vol. 1, p. 21 (my italics).

[10] L. Dussieux, *Etude biographique de Colbert*, Paris, 1886, p. 353, 'Un Christ au jardin par M. Lebrun . . . 400 livres'.

[11] F. Engerand, *Inventaire des tableaux du Roi redigé en 1709 et 1710 par Nicolas Bailly*, Paris, 1899, p. 322, 'un tableau représentant Jesus-Christ soutenu par un ange faisant sa prière au jardin des Olives : un autre ange dans un nuage lui presente le calice accompagné de plusieurs cherubims qui paroissent dans un nuage : figures de demi nature ayant 4 pieds et demi de diamètre'.

[12] Nivelon, *op. cit.*, fol. 147.

[13] Blunt, *op. cit.*, p. 186.

[14] E. Foucart-Walter, *Le Mans, Musée de Tessé : Peintures françaises du XVIIe siècle*, Paris, 1982, p. 93.

Pierre Mignard
Troyes 1612–1695 Paris

Due to the loss of most of his important decorative commissions and the damage affecting many of his remaining history subjects, Mignard stands as one of the best-known names but least understood artists to be First Painter. Today we are most familiar with Mignard the portraitist, and even here our understanding is deformed by the many bad copies and misattributed pictures labled with his name. A pupil of the Bourges painter Jean Boucher, then of Simon Vouet, Mignard moved to Italy in 1635, where he lived until 1657 when he returned to France. That he was successful and prominent is all that is known of his two decades in Rome, from which little work survives. Once back in France he prospered decorating private houses and painting society portraits. Limited by the hegemony of Le Brun, Mignard received his first major Crown commissions – most notably for the Petite Galerie, Versailles (later destroyed) – only after the death of Colbert in 1683. He succeeded Le Brun as Premier Peintre in 1690. Lada Nikolenko published a catalogue of the portraits in 1983; Jean-Claude Boyer is to publish a monograph.

Pierre Mignard

3 *Pan and Syrinx*

Oil on canvas, H.28¾in. w.38½in.
Coll. Martin Desjardins: estimated at 600 livres by Hyacinthe Rigaud,
9 August 1694;[1] Coll. *de trés beaux tableaux, desseins et estampes des
maîtres des trois écoles . . . partie de ces effets viennent de la succession de
feu M. J-B. [sic] de Troy*; sold, Paris, 9 April 1764, no. 95, 160 livres to
M. de Langeac;[2] Coll. Gaspard Barbier de la Bonnetière; sale of Mme
Barbier de la Bonnetière, Nantes, 16 May 1859, no. 254, bought in;
Coll. Charles-Gabriel-Réné-Berlion, Baron de la Tour de Pin Chambly
de la Charce; sale of Baron de la Tour du Pin, Paris, Hôtel Drouot,
26 February 1894, no. 46; the Marquis de Lastic, Paris.

Lent by the Marquis de Lastic, Paris.

The tale of Pan's thwarted assault on Syrinx, who was transformed into a
marsh reed to escape the satyr-god's lust, is the story with which Mercury
finally lulled Argus to sleep and one of the most celebrated and often-
painted episodes in Ovid's *Metamorphoses* (I/668–721). As Jean-Claude
Boyer has pointed out it was practically the only mythological subject to
recur in Mignard's repertory. The story of Pan and Syrinx was one that
Mignard painted several times at the end of his career and which he
imbued with a seriousness that is not altogether apparent upon a first
reading.[3]

Our picture, painted for the Flemish sculptor, Martin Desjardins (1637–
94) – a close friend of Mignard's whose magnificent portrait bust of the
artist is in the Louvre – may be considered the prototype of the *Pan and
Syrinx* series. There is a pentiment visible on Ladon the river god's right
thigh, which shows that Mignard first intended the drapery to extend all
the way across Ladon's body. In changing this detail, Mignard maintained
the almost chromatic effect of flowing drapery alternating with exposed
flesh, which is consistent from the naiad seated by the urn in the left
background to Syrinx herself, caught among the reeds.

Boyer has also shown how this Ovidian tale of desire and its deception was
infused with a sterner morality by Mignard, who is more concerned to
show the brutality of lust and the disastrous consequences of unbridled
passion than to exploit the erotic or decorative potential of the episode
which so appealed to a later generation of French artists – for example,
Jean-François De Troy's *Pan and Syrinx* (J. Paul Getty Museum, Malibu).
For Mignard, the theme had personal implications. He is known to have
bequeathed a painting of this subject to his elder son, Charles – and its
pendant, *Apollo and Daphne*, now lost, to his younger son, Rodolphe – and
this has been convincingly interpreted as an injunction not to marry without paternal approval – both subjects showing, as they do, the havoc
caused by the gods who pursued only their selfish passions.[5] The *Pan and
Syrinx* Mignard painted for his son, recently acquired by the Louvre,
repeats our composition in a vertical format but with important differences
[FIG. 1]. The two river gods, in the foreground, who do not appear in our
painting, express their fear at the violence that is taking place above them.
In the background, the naiads are replaced by a solitary cupid who sits and
extinguishes love's flame, resigned to the awful consequences of Pan's
behavior.

Our painting is not known to have had such intimate implications for the
artist, yet the mood of sorrow and regret remains overpowering. The
naiads look upon the attempted rape with poignant but stoic dismay.
Cupid's feeble attempts at restraining Syrinx are heightened by the huge
reeds which dwarf him and which have already begun to engulf the
nymph. Finally, the contrast of Syrinx's pure white flesh against Pan's

FIG. 1 Mignard, *Pan and Syrinx*, Louvre

58

3 Pierre Mignard, *Pan and Syrinx*

hairy darkness, while conventional, is symbolic both of her terror – which is emphasized by her hair and robe, caught in the wind – and of his brutality.

Within two generations, Mignard's *Pan and Syrinx* would acquire yet another moral gloss, this time far less profound than the artist's ruminations on the danger of irrational desire. The verses which accompanied Edme Jeurat's engraving of our painting, published in 1718, offered a plaint against the lax behavior of women and adultery in general. Syrinx's terror is now revealed to be little more than her horror of Pan's horns, which have since lost their capacity to invoke fear:

> Hideux étoit jadis tel ornement de tête.
> Les choses changent bien! Eût-on dix pieds de crête
> Il n'est Belle en ce jour, qui d'un oeil aguérri,
> Ne les vit, en riant, même sur son mari.

> (Once such horns were considered hideous.. But how things have changed! There is hardly a beauty today who has any difficulty in contemplating them, be they ten feet high, and she can even see them on her husband and still laugh).[6]

Mignard's pondered and troubled reflections on human desire and the need for control of the senses are thus reduced to illustrating a mediocre homily on worldly infidelity.

Mignard is known to have painted at least two others versions of *Pan and Syrinx*. His powerful protector, the *Surintendant des Bâtiments*, François-Michel Le Tellier, Marquis de Louvois (1641–91), owned one of these, estimated at the substantial figure of 500 livres in the inventory of the picture cabinet of the Hôtel Louvois in 1691. Mignard also painted 'deux grands tableaux' towards the end of his career, representing *Pan and Syrinx* and *Apollo and Daphne* for Charles II of Spain – a prestigious commission secured through the intermediary of *Monsieur*. The whereabouts of these three paintings remain unknown.[7]

Notes

[1] L. Seelig, 'L'inventaire après décès de Martin van de Bogaert, dit Desjardins, sculpteur ordinaire du Roi (7 Août 1694)', *B.S.H.A.F.*, 1972, pp. 170–1.

[2] This was a composite sale in which de Troy's estate played a relatively minor part. Our picture is not listed among the effects of the former Director of the Academy of Rome.

[3] Much of this entry is based on Jean-Claude Boyer's excellent article, 'Un chef d'oeuvre retrouvé de Pierre Mignard (1612–95): *Pan et Syrinx*', *Revue du Louvre et des Musées de France*, June 1980, no. 3, pp. 152–6.

[4] L. Seelig, *op. cit.*, pp. 161–82.

[5] Boyer, *op. cit.*, p. 156, note 23.

[6] Bibliothèque Nationale, Cabinet des Estampes, *Db. 27*, fol. 45; reproduced in Boyer, *op. cit.*, p. 154.

[7] Boyer, *op. cit.*, p. 156, note 17.

Antoine Coypel
Écuyer Premier Peintre du Roy
Et de S.A.R. Monseigneur le Duc d'Orléans Régent du Royme
Directeur et Recteur de l'Académie R.
de Peinture et de Sculpture).
Peint par luy même.
Gravé par J.B.Massé pour le Recueil en 1734. attendu

Antoine Coypel
Paris 1661–1722 Paris

From the age of twelve to fourteen, Antoine Coypel lived in Rome with his father and mentor, Nöel, first generation of the Coypel artistic dynasty, who, from 1673 to 1675 was the Director of the Académie de France. This formative Italian journey permanently affected the development of Antoine's art: his personal contact with Carlo Maratta and admiration for Correggio fed his taste for the grand manner and encouraged a cool, refined palette. Accepted into the Academy at the age of twenty, with *Louis XIV after the Peace of Nijmegen* (1681), Antoine launched one of the outstanding official careers of his day. He was a fine draftsman and experimental colorist whose early works are most indebted to Le Brun but whose later paintings reveal an increased appreciation of Rubens. He became First Painter to his patrons, the Orléans family, in 1688; Director of the Academy in 1714; and *Premier Peintre du Roi* in 1715, filling the post left unoccupied since the death of Mignard. Due to increasing infirmity, he painted little following his ennoblement, and it is his earlier religious and mythological compositions for which he is best known, including the decoration of the Galerie d'Enée in the Palais Royal and the Chapel at Versailles, both painted for the Crown from 1702 to 1709. Nicole Garnier is soon to publish a study of the artist.

Antoine Coypel

4 *Christ Served by the Angels*

Oil on canvas, H.40¼in. w.32¼in.

Coll. Early provenance unknown; Private Collection, Switzerland; Stair Sainty Matthiesen

Exhibition: Paris, Galerie Hahn, *La peinture narrative en France*, 3 March–31 March 1972, no. 4.

Christ Served by the Angels is the earliest painting by Antoine Coypel to have survived.[1] Painted after his return to Paris following a three-year stay in Italy (1673–6), it belongs to the group of religious works that secured this young artist's reputation. The most notable of these included the prestigious May commission for Notre-Dame de Paris – *The Assumption of the Virgin*, 1680 – and three pictures for the Church of the Assumption, painted the following year. All these pictures are now lost.

Although his son would later write that these first paintings convinced the public 'qu'il avoit utilement employé son temps en Italie', *Christ Served by the Angels* owes more to examples nearer home. The composition is closely based on Le Brun's painting of the same subject, painted in 1653 for the Carmelite convent and which the young Coypel would have known from the very start of his career [FIG. 1].[2] The influence of the artist's father, Noël Coypel – who as the Director of the Academy at Rome took his eleven-year-old son to Italy in 1672 to complete his training – is also apparent in the treatment of the figure of Christ and the angel on the right. Thus, in its classical handling of drapery, its borrowed vocabulary of gestures and expressions, and its cool, almost acidic range of oranges, green-blues and yellows, Coypel's *oeuvre de jeunesse* has been described by his most recent historian as 'encore très archaïque'.[3]

FIG. 1 Lebrun,
Christ Served by the Angels, Louvre

The theme represented is recounted several times in the New Testament, and was treated by Coypel on several occasions throughout his career.[4] It is the story of Christ's temptation in the desert by Satan, who starves him for forty days and nights and urges him to prove his divinity by performing miracles which will alleviate his suffering. Satan finally declares himself defeated when Christ refuses the riches of the world, and on his departure Christ is brought nourishment by the angels. Le Brun's picture actually depicts one of these pulling the hair of the retreating devil. Coypel's composition is pared of any detailed allusion to the biblical passage, although the rocks upon which Christ and the angels sit are perhaps a reference to those which the devil encourages him to change into food in order to assuage his hunger.

Another known composition by Coypel of the same subject is in the Musée de Châlons-sur-Marne, dated a decade later to 1690–5 [FIG. 2].[5] While the elements are the same, the treatment and handling of the composition could not be more different. From the meticulously articulated but schematic drawing of the early picture, Coypel has now developed a more fluid and painterly style, much indebted to Flemish art in general and Rubens in particular, and entirely independent of the influence of Le Brun or Noël Coypel.

FIG. 2 A. Coypel,
Christ Served by the Angels,
Châlons-sur-Marne

In the absence of engravings or any recorded commission, it is difficult to assign a precise date for the early *Christ Served by the Angels*. Coypel had painted at least one similar subject before 1683: Mariette mentioned that a *Christ Praying in the Garden of Olives* was engraved by Guillaume Chasteau, who died in that year. Nicole Garnier has dated this work to around 1680,

4 Antoine Coypel, *Christ Served by the Angels*

dating that has also been suggested elsewhere.[6] It should be noted that Coypel used the same seated figure in his earliest documented painting, *Louis XIV Resting in the Lap of Glory after the Peace of Nijmegen* (Musée Fabre, Montpellier), his *morceau de réception* of 1681 [FIG. 3]. This helps substantiate a dating to the early 1680's.

Notes

[1] N. Garnier, *Antoine Coypel (1661–1722): l'homme, l'art et l'oeuvre*, thèse pour l'Ecole des Chartes, Paris, 1979, catalogue no. 1. I am extremely grateful to Mlle Garnier for allowing me to consult her thesis which is shortly to be published.

[2] J. Thuillier and J. Montagu, *Charles Le Brun*, exhib. cat., Versailles, 1963, no. 18. The *Christ Served by the Angels* is in the Louvre, Paris.

[3] Garnier, *op. cit.*, catalogue no. 1.

[4] Apart from the version here and the version in Châlons-sur-Marne, there is an engraving by J-B. Bonnart which is close to the latter but with additional elements. Among Coypel's effects at his death are listed, somewhat ambiguously, 'deux tableaux copiés M. Antoine Coypel [*sic*] l'un representant Notre Seigneur servi dans les desert par les anges', A.N., *Minutier Central*, XLIX 502, Inventaire après décès, 19 January 1722.

[5] Garnier, *op. cit.*, catalogue no. 44.

[6] J. Hahn, *La peinture narrative en France, 1500–1800*, (exhib. cat.), Paris, 1972, p. 6.

Antoine Coypel

5 *The Finding of Moses*

Oil on canvas, H.44⅞in. W.57½in.

Coll. Early provenance unknown; Heim Gallery, London, 1977; The Allen Memorial Art Musuem, Oberlin, Ohio.

Lent by The Allen Memorial Art Museum, Oberlin, Ohio.

Exhibitions: Paris Salons 1699, 1704; London, Heim Gallery, *Aspects of French Academic Art, 1680–1780*, Summer 1977, no. 5.

During the 1690's Antoine Coypel produced a series of ambitious but relatively small-scale history paintings of episodes from the Old Testament. These were painted for various highly placed Parisian *amateurs*, since the finances of the Crown – Coypel's major patron in the 1680's – were now entirely devoted to Louis XIV's war against the Grand Alliance, which would be concluded, to his disadvantage, by the Treaty of Ryswick in 1697.[1] This major shift in patronage coincided with an equally momentous aesthetic change for the artist. Through his association with the Duc de Richelieu, whose taste had undergone 'a spectacular conversion from Poussin to Rubens', Coypel was exposed to the work of the latter with far-reaching consequences for his own style, which Antoine Schnapper has analyzed as experiencing a 'crisis of Rubensism' in the early 1690's.[2]

By mid-decade Coypel was able to synchronize the lessons of Poussin and Rubens more felicitously, and the Old Testament series is his most successful attempt at such reconciliation. Our picture, dated to around 1696–7 and exhibited in the Salons of 1699 and 1704, treats the popular theme of the Finding of Moses. It has already been noted that Coypel chose to paint the episode in which Moses' sister arrives with his real mother, who offers to nurse the child, rather than the more traditional episode in which Pharoah's daughter and her attendants come across the infant in the bullrushes.[3]

But Coypel's fidelity to the text should be emphasized. He has represented the scene described in Exodus 2:9. Moses' sister has just returned with a wet-nurse for the baby from among the Hebrew women,

> And Pharoah's daughter said unto her, Take this child away and nurse it for me, and I will give thee thy wages. And the woman took the child and nursed it.

We see Pharoah's daughter in a suitably majestic pose, and most important, Moses' mother, bearing her breast as if about to suckle the child, confirms the precision of Coypel's biblical quotation. This is the dramatic moment of a story which generally offered painters the opportunity to depict an assembly of elegant, beautifully clad young women whose decorative potential was valued above the spiritual associations of the episode. Compare, for example, Charles de La Fosse's version of the subject [FIG. 1], painted a few years later, where the rhythmical, gracious grouping of the young women is unconnected with the climax of the story as told in Exodus.[4]

Here was Coypel's originality, questionable in terms of what was pictorially effective, but crucial if his narrative pictures, often excessively theatrical and staged to modern eyes, are to be understood. In his own words:

> The painter must respect the rules of the art of declamation if he is to bring together (*accorder*) gestures and facial expressions. . . . Unable to endow his figures with the gift of speech, he needs must compensate by the lively expression of gestures and actions, rather like those which deaf mutes employ to make themselves understood.[5]

Thus the complex emotions of relief and delight at having saved the infant

FIG. 1 C. de la Fosse, *The Finding of Moses*, Louvre

FIG. 2 N. Poussin, *The Finding of Moses*, Louvre   FIG. 3 N. Poussin, *The Finding of Moses*, Louvre

Moses by well-meaning subterfuge are registered by Moses' sister who stands behind the group in the center. Moses' mother looks with fondness at her own child, while at the same time bowing her head in respect and gratitude before Pharoah's daughter.

Coypel assimilated classical sources as well as contemporary theatricality in his *Finding of Moses*. He has looked to Poussin both for the landscape and architectural background [FIG. 2], as well as the gesture of Pharoah's daughter and the horizontal grouping of the female attendants [FIG. 3]. Yet the striking juxtaposition of bright colors, the attention to the sheen of the draperies and a certain exoticism in Pharoah's daughter's apparel, as well as the dynamism of the composition, are resolutely modern and anti-Poussinist in conception.

Although there are no preparatory drawings for Coypel's *Finding of Moses*, certain drawings can be connected with individual figures in the composition. To those proposed by Schnapper can be added a *Study of a Woman* (Cabinet des Dessins, Louvre) [FIG. 4], which, while originally conceived as a naiade, may well have served as the model for the woman at the extreme right of the painting, who guards the infant's basket.[6]

FIG. 4 A. Coypel, *Study of a Woman*, Cabinet des Dessins, Louvre

Nor do we know for whom Coypel painted the *Finding of Moses*. Jean Audran's engraving after this picture was dedicated to César d'Estrées, the powerful and cultivated cardinal who had protected Coypel since the 1670's, and would return to Paris in 1693 for a period of seven years.[7] A study of César d'Estrées' patronage might yield some clue as to the early provenance of this picture. Finally, it is worth mentioning that the Dutartre sale of 19 March 1804 included two paintings 'd'une riche ordonnance' representing *The Finding of Moses* and the *Judgment of Solomon* but given to Noël Coypel. Not only are the dimensions almost identical to the Oberlin picture – H. 41in. W. 53in. in the Dutartre catalogue – but the *Judgment of Solomon* was one of the nine Old Testament themes painted by Coypel and catalogued by Schnapper, exhibited at the same Salons as *The Finding of Moses* and now lost.[8]

Notes

[1] N. Garnier, *op. cit.*, cat. no. 64.

[2] A. Schnapper, 'The Moses of Antoine Coypel', *Allen Memorial Art Museum Bulletin*, 37, 1979–80, p. 61.

[3] *Aspects of French Academic Art, 1680–1780*, London, 1977, cat. no. 5.

[4] M. Stuffman, 'Charles de la Fosse et sa position dans la peinture française à la fin du XVIIe siècle', *GBA*, 64, 1964, pp. 48–52.

[5] A. Coypel. *Discours prononcé dans les conférences de l'Académie Royale de Peinture et de Sculpture*, Paris, 1721, pp. 63–4.

[6] Schnapper, *op. cit.*, p. 66, fig. 8. Coypel's *Study of a Woman* INV 25712 is reproduced in Guiffrey and Marcel, *Inventaire général des Dessins du Louvre et du Musée de Versailles*, Paris, 1921, vol. 3, no. 3057.

[7] 'L'Oeuvre gravé des Coypel, II', *GBA*, 64, 1964, no. 6, p. 142, wrongly given to Coypel himself.

[8] A. Paillet, *Catalogue des tableaux, marbres, bronzes, vases précieux . . . composant le cabinet de feu M. Dutartre, Ancien Tresorier des Bâtiments*, Paris, 19 March 1804, no. 42. The pendants were sold for 301 livres according to the annotated catalogue at the Bibliothèque Nationale.

5 Antoine Coypel, *The Finding of Moses*

Louis de Boullongne II
Paris 1654–1733 Paris

Heir to a considerable fortune, Boullongne was the son of one of the founders of the Academy, Louis de Boullongne I, as well as his pupil. In Rome from 1675 to 1680, where he copied Raphael and the Bolognese masters, he was received into the Academy in 1681 with *Augustus Closing the Temple of Janus* (Amiens). Inevitably influenced by Le Brun, he was one of the first painters to respond openly to Dutch and Flemish seventeenth-century painters. He did extensive work for the Crown, notably in the Chapel at Versailles and the Châteaux of Fontainebleau and Trianon and was a fine technician and brilliant draftsman. He exhibited numerous works at the Salons of 1699 and 1704, nearly all religious or mythological subjects but also a few portraits. He gradually broke away from the reddish palette of his contemporaries, using clearer, more Rubensian colors, and adopted a tighter, more distinctive style, although he lacked real invention in his compositions. Ennobled in 1724, he was made First Painter in 1725.

Louis de Boullongne

6 *Venus Commanding Vulcan to Make Arms for Aeneas*

Oil on canvas, H.26⅞in. w.22⅛in.
Signed lower left corner: *Boulogne jeune, 1703*.

Coll. Early provenance unknown; sold, Paris, Hôtel Drouot, Me Renaud,
8 March 1985, no. 2, *Venus dans la Forge de Vulcan*; Stair Sainty
Matthiesen.

Between August 1698 and August 1700 the architect Jules-Hardouin
Mansart supervised the transformation of the interior of the Château de la
Ménagerie, which the ageing Louis XIV had offered to Adelaide of Savoy –
the child bride of his grandson, the Duc de Bourgogne – who had so
captivated the monarch since her arrival at Versailles in 1697. Mansart was
responsible for redecorating the two principal *appartements* of the château –
an *appartement d'été* and an *appartement d'hiver*. In all, fifteen members of
the Académie Royale de Peinture were employed to paint appropriate
subjects for insertion into *boiseries* that were themselves decorated with
grotesques by Claude III Audran. The history of the commission and the
fate of the thirty-six decorative panels, which do not concern us here, have
been very fully documented by Gérard Mabille.[1]

The major room in the *appartement d'été*, the Duchess' bedchamber, was
decorated by the most prominent of the artists employed on the project.
Bon Boullongne, Louis de Boullongne and Antoine Coypel all painted
themes relating to Venus, goddess of love. Furthermore, and as was suitable for the winter *appartements*, the story of Venus commissioning arms
from Vulcan also served to symbolize the element of Fire. The iconography
of the painting nicely mirrored the dual function of the particular setting.

Our painting, signed and dated 1703, repeats the overdoor Louis de
Boullongne painted for the Château de la Ménagerie, and is the only
known autograph version of a theme he would paint many times in his
career. It reproduces exactly the scene he painted for the Duchesse de
Bourgogne, known today from a contemporary copy in the Musée de
Fontainebleau, which is considerably larger than the original version.[2]

It is extremely tempting to relate our picture to the Ménagerie overdoor
itself. We know that Boullongne received payment for this overdoor and its
pendant – *Venus Giving Arms to Aeneas* (copy, Musée Rigaud, Perpignan)
– as late as January 1705.[3] Yet Mabille has argued convincingly that, if the
pictures were the last element in the decorative scheme to be executed and
affixed, there is good reason to believe that they were *in situ* by the winter
of 1700. In December of that year Louis XIV accompanied the Duchesse
de Bourgogne on a visit to the recently completed *appartements* which, we
are told, he found 'magnificent and charming'.[4] Our canvas is approxi-
mately the same width as the Ménagerie overdoor, but considerably
smaller in height. Finally, unlike the other originals that have survived,
there are no signs that our canvas was once of oval format.

Louis XIV rejected the subjects Mansart initially proposed for the various
rooms of the two main *appartements* in a riposte that has become famous.
Thinking of the thirteen-year-old Princess for whom the residence was
intended, the King is recorded as saying, 'there must be youthfulness in all
that is done in these *appartements* . . . there must be childhood reflected
everywhere'.[5] And indeed, in his interpretation of this stock decorative
subject, Boullongne has infused an overtly erotic episode with a sweetness
and gaiety both delicate and innocent. The smiling cupid who stares
directly at us while holding his mistress' trail; the white dove who pecks
around on the ground beneath him; the slightly disgruntled expression on

Vulcan's face as he receives orders from his imperious spouse – these details, combined with a refined, but brightly colored palette, go to make one of Boullongne's freshest decorative inventions.

Several versions of this subject are recorded in eighteenth-century catalogues, notably a set of mythological paintings of the four elements in the sale of 'M.XXX' (15 May 1786) where *Venus Commanding Arms for Vulcan* was explicitly listed as representing Fire.[6] This may have been the same subject engraved by Louis Desplaces in 1717: a horizontal composition which depicts Venus and the graces confronting Vulcan and the Cyclops in a more traditional juxtaposition.[7] A preparatory drawing for the subject engraved by Desplaces, as well as a group of black-and-white chalk studies for the Cyclops in this composition, are in the Cabinet des Dessins, Louvre (Inv. 24950–5). Two further drawings of *Venus Giving Arms to Aeneas*, preparatory for Boullongne's decorative commissions at Meudon and Trianon respectively (Inv. 24957 and 24963), repeat the subject of our painting's pendant, but with the elements differently arranged.[8] Finally, the popularity of the subject is attested by the numerous copies after Louis de Boullongne's paintings of Venus and Vulcan recorded in Daniel Wildenstein's anthology of collectors' inventories.[9]

Notes

[1] G. Mabille, 'La Ménagerie de Versailles', *GBA*, Jan. 1974, pp. 5–36; *idem*, 'Les tableaux de la Menagérie de Versailles', *BSHAF*, année 1974 (1975), pp. 89–101.

[2] Reproduced in Mabille, 'Les tableaux . . .', *op. cit.*, p. 94.

[3] *Comptes des Bâtiments du Roi sous le règne de Louis XIV, 1664–1715*, ed. J. Guiffrey, 5 vols, Paris, 1881–1901, vol. 4, column 1183. Boullongne was paid 1,000 livres for the two overdoors.

[4] Mabille, 'La Ménagerie de Versailles', *op. cit.*, p. 24.

[5] *Idem*, 'Les tableaux . . .', *op. cit.*, p. 90.

[6] *Catalogue de tableaux des écoles d'Italie, des Pays Bas et de France provenans du cabinet de MXXX*, Paris, 15 May 1786, no. 52, H. 3 pieds 2 pouces, W. 4 pieds 3 pouces.

[7] Caix de Saint-Aymour, Cte de, *Les Boullongne*, Paris, 1919, no. 489, where it is incorrectly listed as the same subject as the Ménagerie overdoor.

[8] Guiffrey-Marcel, *op. cit.*, vol. 2, nos. 1443–6 (ill.).

[9] D. Wildenstein, *Inventaires après décès d'artistes et de collectionneurs français du XVIIIe siècle*, Paris, 1967, nos. 94, 98 and 101.

6 Louis de Boullongne, *Venus Commanding Vulcan to Make Arms for Aeneas*

Louis de Boullongne

7 *Rinaldo and Armida*

Oil on canvas, H.38in. w.51½in.
Signed and dated on inner rim of fountain: *Louis de Boullongne pinxit 1704.*

Coll. (?) Jean de Boullongne, inventory of estate, 7 Mar 1769, 'un autre du même (Louis de Boullongne) representant Renaud et Armide prisé trois cent cinquante livres'[1]; M.XXX, sold Paris, 18–20 April 1785, no. 108 (*Note sur les Tableaux de bons Maîtres des Ecoles d'Italie, des Pays Bas et de France du cabinet de M.XXX*)[2]; nineteenth-century provenance unknown; Les Andelys, Eure, *Hôtel des Ventes*, 13 Nov 1983; Stair Sainty Matthiesen.

Exhibition: Salon 1704.

The story of Rinaldo and Armida in the Enchanted Palace (Book XVI) was the most frequently depicted scene from Torquato Tasso's epic poem *Gerusalemme Liberata*, first published in 1581 – a work which inspired masterpieces from Domenichino, Poussin and Van Dyck, to name but three of the many seventeenth- and eighteenth-century artists who would interpret episodes from Tasso's story.

Louis de Boullongne's *Rinaldo and Armida*, painted in 1704 and exhibited in the Salon of that year, follows Tasso's text with remarkable fidelity. Hiding behind the trees on the left of the canvas we see Ubaldo and Carlo, the two Danish knights who have come to release their companion, Rinaldo, the Crusaders' champion. Captured by the Saracen princess, Armida, who has fallen hopelessly in love with him, Rinaldo has been transported by her to her Enchanted Palace on the Fortunate Isles, where,

> in perpetual, sweet and flouring Spring
> she lives at Ease and joyes her Lord at will (14:71).[3]

The Danish knights have been given magical instruments which allow them to enter this protected domain: Carlo holds a golden staff and Ubaldo carries the diamond shield that he will use to break Armida's spell over their leader. The spectacle of Rinaldo's amorous enslavement, witnessed by the knights, forms the opening to Book 16 and is the scene represented here. Armida is scantily clad – 'her Breasts were naked for the Day was hot' – and she adjusts her hair:

> O'er him her looks she hung and her soft Breast
> The Pillow was, where he and love took rest (16:18).

Such is Rinaldo's infatuation that while Armida looks into the crystal mirror that he holds for her, he can do nothing but gaze at her reflection: 'he . . . both beauty and love beheld, both in one seat' (16:20).

Boullongne's painting conveys the sweet eroticism of this romantic idyll with great assurance. He has looked to Domenichino's *Rinaldo and Armida* (Louvre) [FIG. 1] – which entered Louis XIV's collection in 1685 – for the general composition and for details such as the Danish knights behind the trees, the amoretti who surround the lovers and the double-tiered colonnade in the background. Yet the garlands of flowers strewn across Rinaldo's armor and draped around his waist are not only a reference to Armida's magic chains of 'Woodbines, Lilies and Roses sweet' (14:68), they also serve a decorative purpose in keeping with the function of the picture itself. For Boullongne's picture was used as a model for one of the Gobelin's *Metamorphoses* series, a *petite tenture* of 1704 comprising subjects by Bertin, de La Fosse and Antoine Coypel, many of which were taken from decorative paintings already in Royal residences.[4] Boullongne's *Rinaldo and Armida* was greatly extended in the tapestry cartoon painted by Yvart fils, Chastelain and Belin de Fontenay [FIG. 2]. Here the main figures are almost dwarfed by the luxuriant vegetation, the peacocks on the right and the Fountain of Laughter on the left – all elements with obvious decorative

7 Louis de Boullongne, *Rinaldo and Armida*

FIG. 1 Domenichino, *Rinaldo and Armida*, Louvre

FIG. 2 Wart fils, tapestry cartoon *Rinaldo and Armida*, Galerie Chevalier, Paris

FIG. 3 Boucher, *Rinaldo and Armida*, Louvre

FIG. 4 A. Coypel, *Rinaldo and Armida*

appeal. The tapestry, unlike Boullongne's painting, reduces the impending drama still further by relegating Carlo and Ubaldo, the knights who will break Armida's spell, to an almost invisible position behind the balustrade in the background.

All of the eighteenth-century *Premier Peintres* treated subjects from Tasso's *Gerusalemme Liberata*: either as a decorative suite – Van Loo's eleven panels for the Palazzo Reale, Turin; an academic set piece – Boucher's *morceau de réception* of 1734 [FIG. 3]; or competition entry – Pierre's *Rinaldo and Armida* for the 1747 *concours*. Yet Louis de Boullongne's tightly painted and gently rhythmical composition, with its boyish putti and airy foliage, is among the most successful in recreating an atmosphere of untrammelled pleasure, soon to end. Rinaldo's adoring expression as he gazes up at Armida, whose reflection we see in the mirror he holds, is both moving and convincing. If Boullongne's conception of passion is characteristically *gracieux*, his interpretation of this theme eschews both the declamatory and the rhetorical – for example, Antoine Coypel's *Rinaldo and Armida* [FIG. 4] seems mawkish and somewhat overloaded by comparison. With his palette of cold blues, purples and reds, Boullongne transforms Tasso's fantastical drama into an arcadian refuge for innocent passion.

FIG. 5 Boullongne, *Rinaldo and Armida*,
Private Collection, New York

FIG. 6 Boullongne, *Male figure study*, J. B. Speed Art Museum

Our picture was sufficiently well-known in the first half of the eighteenth century to inspire at least one full-scale copy, recorded in the collection of Mme Galloys, 15 March 1764, no. 15. A smaller version was noted in the second Conti sale (15 March 1779, no. 65) as part of a series of literary and mythological lovers.[5] It is quite possible that our picture itself remained in Louis de Boullongne's possession after being exhibited in the Salon of 1704 and used for the *Metamorphosis* tapestry: nowhere is it referred to as having been purchased by the Crown. Rather, it may well have passed to the artist's elder son, Jean de Boullongne (1690–1769), the powerful and wealthy *Intendant des Finances*, who was briefly *Contrôleur-Général* at the start of the Seven years' war.[6] Jean de Boullongne owned eight major pictures by his father, among which a *Rinaldo and Armida* valued as 350 livres – a reasonable estimation – but with no indication of dimensions.[7] Our painting is last documented in the *cabinet* of an anonymous collector who sent his pictures to be sold in Paris, by Remy, between 18–20 April 1785.[8] A small-scale variant of our *Rinaldo and Armida*, possibly with studio assistance, has appeared recently on the market [FIG. 5]. The J. B. Speed Art Museum, Louisville, Kentucky, has a fine black-and-white chalk drawing, preparatory for the figure of the reclining Rinaldo, who holds the stem of Armida's mirror [FIG. 6].

Notes

[1] A.N., *Minutier Central*, LIII/446, *Inventaire après décès, Jean de Boullongne*, 7 March 1769.

[2] No. 108 'Renaud et Armide par Louis de Boulogne [*sic*] sur toile de trois pieds de haut, quatre pieds de large'.

[3] All quotations are from Edward Fairfax's translation, *Godfrey of Bulloigne, or the Recovery of Jerusalem*, London, 1687.

[4] M. Fenaille, *Etat Général des Tapisseries de la Manufacture des Gobelins; Dixhuitième Siècle, Première Partie, 1699–1736*, Paris, 1904, pp. 121–34.

[5] I owe both of these references to Alastair Laing.

[6] Caix de St Aymour, *op. cit.*, pp. 123–37 *passim*.

[7] *Inventaire après décès, op. cit.*

[8] This catalogue, which is hard to locate, is LUGT 3862. I consulted the copy in the Institut de France, *8 Duplessis, no. 344*.

François Le Moyne
Paris 1688–1738 Paris

Le Moyne's first artistic training came from his stepfather, the portraitist Robert Tournières, whose violent temper lost him both a student and a wife. Beginning in 1701 and for the next twelve years, Le Moyne trained under Galloche. He won the *Grand Prix* in 1711 with a *Ruth and Boaz* but did not go to Italy for another twelve years. He was received into the Academy in 1718 with a *Hercules and Cacus* (Ecole des Beaux Arts, Paris). With his patron François Berger, former Receiver-General of Finances, Le Moyne finally made his Italian sojourn, travelling through Bologna, Rome and Venice and absorbing the lessons of Parmigianino and Veronese and Italian ceiling painting, while completing *Hercules and Omphale* (Louvre, Paris), one of his most successful erotic mythologies. Upon his return he painted *Aurora and Cephalus* for Versailles. He shared first prize in the 1727 Concours with Jean-François De Troy, cementing his position as the leading contemporary French painter. Between 1728 and 1736 he executed his greatest commission, the *Apotheosis of Hercules* in the Salon de la Paix, Versailles. Four days after the finished Salon was unveiled for Louis XV, Le Moyne was made *Premier Peintre du Roi*. Although a memorable draftsman and one of the great colorists of his age, Le Moyne was extremely ambitious and highly self-critical. His mental state degenerated and, haunted by paranoid delusions, the artist took his own life the following year, at the age of forty-nine. He is often remembered today as the teacher of Natoire and Boucher, but his own easel paintings and decorations rival the best works of his famous pupils. Jean-Luc Bordeaux has published the catalogue raisonné of Le Moyne's work.

François Le Moyne

8 *Hercules and Omphale*

Oil on canvas, H.54¾in. W.38¼in.

Coll. Early provenance unknown; Private German Collection; sold Sotheby's, London, 4 April 1984, no. 29; Stair Sainty Matthiesen.

Resting from his twelve labors after returning to Thebes, Hercules became embroiled with the family of Eurytus, whose daughter, Iole, he had won unfairly in an archery contest. Hercules brutally murdered Iphitus, one of Eurytus' sons, who had consented to be his guest, and the god was then forced to seek absolution for having violated the sacred rites of hospitality. Finally, the pythoness, Xenoclea, consented to grant Hercules peace on the condition that he sell himself into slavery for one year and give the sum fetched by his enslavement to Iphitus' children. Hercules was purchased by Omphale, Queen of Lydia, whom he served for one year, largely in the capacity of a willing lover – although he also found time to rid Lydia of a man-eating serpent and a murderous farmer. Omphale so subjugated Hercules that rumour reached Greece that he had taken to dressing in female attire, and would weave and spin in the company of Omphale's attendants.

This story, told by Apollodorus and Ovid, but known in France through Noel Lecomte's *Mythologie*, a copy of which was listed in Le Moyne's library, provided the artist with the subject of his masterpiece.[1] Le Moyne's *Hercules and Omphale* [FIG. 1] (Louvre), painted in 1724 for his protector, François Berger, while they were travelling together in Rome, has Hercules seated on a rock, a distaff in his left hand, a spindle in his right. Omphale, arching her pearly-white body against Hercules massive, ruddy frame, lets her golden tresses fall upon his right shoulder as she lowers her head towards his. She is draped in the lion's pelt he has discarded and holds his huge club suggestively at her side. A winged cupid, in attendance, hands Hercules a bowl of sweets; the setting sun in the background indicates that night is about to fall.

Our picture, which Jean-Luc Bordeaux has described as 'absolutely authentic and brilliantly executed', is the *répétition* of the Louvre's painting and in quite a different category to the many copies that are known. Dezallier d'Argenville, who was a friend of Le Moyne's, reserved a place apart for 'les sujets repétés', which were not mere copies 'et qui ne lassent pas d'être originaux'. 'Rarely', he wrote,

> does a fine artist repeat himself without adding something new. This can take the form of a change in the background, a figure added or taken away, a drapery painted in a different color, anything, in a word, that shows that his picture, even though it repeats the subject, is as original as the first version.[2]

In our *Hercules and Omphale* we find several such changes. Cupid looks straight out at us – his head is at an angle in the Louvre's painting – and his golden locks have changed to waves of hair. To the left foreground of our composition we find creamy, thickly-painted plants, and the clump directly beneath Hercules' cloth of gold and satin brocade does not appear in the Louvre version. Finally, the spatial relationship between the ball of wool and the drapery that frames the top right of our canvas – which was probably cut down both on the top and the left-hand side – is again quite different from that in the prime version, where the edge of the curtain seems to glance against the newly-spun wool.

Discussing the influence of Italian art on the artist during his long-awaited visit to Rome in 1723–4, Mariette noted Le Moyne's debt to Veronese and Parmigianino: and the sinuous Omphale does bear some resemblance to the latter's long-necked Madonnas.[3] Caylus, on the other hand, mentioned

FIG. 1 Le Moyne,
Hercules and Omphale, Louvre

FIG. 2 Boucher, *Hercules and Omphale*, Pushkin Museum, Moscow

Michaelangelo and Pietro da Cortona for the impact their ceiling decorations had on the mature Le Moyne. And the massive bulk of Hercules, does recall, in the most general way, the sculptural male figures of the Sistine Chapel.[4] Yet, despite the antecedents in Italian and Flemish art, Le Moyne's *Hercules and Omphale* is shockingly new in its almost overpowering sensuality. Whereas the story of Hercules' seduction had been related with some contempt in Lecomte's anthology – 'thus, the formerly invincible hero was reduced to doing things that were unworthy of him, and all for the love of a whore' was the author's terse conclusion – Le Moyne produced an image where carnality and expectation are finely balanced.[5] It was Le Moyne's *Hercules and Omphale* which provided a model for the next generation of French artists: Boucher's intensely erotic *Hercules and Omphale* (Pushkin Museum, Moscow) [FIG. 2] is inconceivable without the example of his teacher.

The dating of this *répétition* and the history of its provenance are vexed issues. Le Moyne exhibited a *Hercules and Omphale* at the Salon of 1725, whose dimensions as given then were slightly smaller than the painting owned by Berger and now in the Louvre. It is most unlikely that the Salon painting was our version, since it was a good ten inches larger all round.[6] Furthermore, we are told that Le Moyne worked slowly. His pictures 'lui ont toujours infiniment coûté' (Caylus); Le Moyne was 'fort long dans l'exécution de ses ouvrages' (de Valory).[7] Given that the artist was engaged on decoration at both the Church of Saint Thomas d'Aquin and the Hôtel du Grand Maître, Versailles, it seems plausible to suggest that Berger loaned his *Hercules and Omphale* to the Paris Salon and that Le Moyne was commissioned to paint this *répétition* at some point thereafter. His most devoted pupil, the portraitist Donat Nonnotte, recalled being given just such a commission himself after Berger's painting was seen to great effect in Rome.[8] Our version, then, should be dated later rather than earlier in the 1720's, around 1726, and the somewhat flattened expression of the cupid – a facial type reminiscent of Natoire, another of Le Moyne's pupils – might also suggest that the master was here responding to the latest style of a younger generation that he himself had trained.

There are two preparatory drawings for the figure of Omphale: the majestic torso in the British Museum, once given to Watteau, and an exquisite red-and-black chalk head, with certain differences in detail, in the Berkeley University Art Museum. A drawing done after the *Hercules and Omphale*, with separate elements of the painting in reverse, is at the Ecole des Beaux Arts, Paris.[9]

Notes

[1] J-L. Bordeaux, *François Le Moyne (1688–1737) and his generation*, Neuilly-sur-Seine, 1984, no. 47, pp. 93–5.

[2] A. J. Dezallier d'Argenville, *Abrégé de la Vie des plus fameux peintres*, deuxième édition, 4 vols, Paris, 1762, vol. 1, pp. xlii–xliii.

[3] P. J. Mariette, *Abécedario*, ed. P. de Chennevières and A. de Montaiglon, 6 vols, Paris, 1851–60, vol. 3, p. 132.

[4] A. Fontaine, *Comte de Caylus: Vie d'Artistes du XVIIIe siècle*, Paris, 1910, p. 54.

[5] *Mytholgie, c'est à dire Explication des fables, contenant les généalogies des dieux . . . extraite du latin de Noël le Comte*, 2 vols, Lyon, 1604, vol. 2, p. 675.

[6] J-L. Bordeaux, *op. cit.*, p. 95 gives a well-balanced discussion of this problem.

[7] Fontaine, *op. cit.*, p. 45.

[8] J. Gauthier, 'Donat Nonnotte: Vie du peintre François Lemoyne', *Réunion des Sociétés des Beaux Arts des Départements*, 26, 1902, p. 533.

[9] J-L. Bordeaux, *op. cit.*, pp. 154–5, drawings nos. 65 and 66.

8 François Le Moyne, *Hercules and Omphale*

François Le Moyne

9 *The Amorous Proposal*

Oil on canvas, H.39in. W.57in.

Coll. M. de XXX, sold Paris, 'Cabinet de M. Pelt, Ecuyer, et de celui de M. de XXX', 21 Feb 1774, no. 105, 1,240 livres; The Earls of Gainsborough, England; Count William de Belleroche; F. R. D. Byfield; J. Carras; Christie's, London, 15 Apr 1984, no. 92 (unsold); Stair Sainty Matthiesen.

Exhibitions: London, Royal Academy, European Masters of the Eighteenth Century, 1954–5, no. 129; London, Colnaghi, *Art, Commerce, Scholarship*, 7 November–15 December 1984, no. 57.

Le Moyne's sumptuously executed scene of a young woman wringing a cloth in a fountain while being approached by an older, bearded man in Turkish dress, has presented problems almost since the time it was painted.[1] First, the subject is unknown. Entitled *l'amant suranné* in Géraud Vidal's engraving after a second version of this picture, it was given no title at all when Pierre Remy catalogued it in the collection of M. de XXX (21 February 1774). The various versions, which will be discussed later, were subsequently connected with episodes from the Old Testament and the scene has been interpreted as Rebecca and Eleazar, Abraham and Hagar and Susannah at the Fountain. The picture's overt gallantry and provocative allusions argue against a scriptural source. Rather, the play between age, sex and race finds expression in one of Le Moyne's favored antitheses: the enamel-white skin of the golden-haired maiden juxtaposed with the swarthy, hirsute, muscular Turk whose right hand rests, paw-like, on her shoulder.

If the subject of this picture was lost early on, there has been similar confusion as to its authorship. Four years after Remy catalogued our picture, a second version appeared in the Briard sale (7 January 1778), praised as 'd'une touche fraîche, d'une couleur transparente', but given to Le Moyne with some hesitation: 'on l'estime être de F. Le Moyne'.[2] Our picture was attributed to Jean-François De Troy for most of the nineteenth century and only restored to Le Moyne in 1955.[3]. The second version appeared in a recent sale as by Noël-Nicolas Coypel, and Vidal's engraving was catalogued among the lost works of Carle Van Loo. As Alastair Laing pointed out, this confusion was partly understandable, given Le Moyne's manner here which anticipates the generation of Natoire and Pierre.[4]. The richly impasted drapery; the undisguised textural strokes of the Turk's head, beard and neck; the dramatic, yet warm luminosity of the composition as a whole all recall the mature style of Le Moyne's great rival, Jean-François De Troy, and in particular the Esther series, painted between 1738 and 1740, well over a decade later. Yet the checkered history of this picture also reflects the singular neglect that many early eighteenth-century French painters, and especially history painters, have received until very recently. Eighteenth-century opinion was better informed. Remy had no doubts about this 'distinguished picture' – the words are his – and his assessment of its quality was apt and still serves: 'la touche en est large et le coloris admirable'.[5]

Three versions of this painting are known, as well as a replica of the young woman at the fountain (Hôtel Drouot, 10 December 1980, no. 11). The *Susannah at the Fountain* (Musée du Berry, Bourges) is generally accepted as a copy, but opinion is divided over our picture, known as the Belleroche version, and a second painting, formerly in the Krichewsky collection, and catalogued by Bordeaux as the prime version [FIG. 1].[6] The latter, with its warm, golden tonality and even larger handling – the foliage is abbreviated, almost sketched in – also differs from ours in certain details. The

9 François Le Moyne, *The Amorous Proposal*

FIG. 1 Le Moyne, *The Amorous Proposal*

FIG. 2 Le Moyne, *Christ and the Woman of Samaria*, Cathedral of Sens

fountain appears with its inward curving volute clearly visible, whereas this ornament is covered by foliage in our painting. There are also minor differences in the treatment of the wall to the right of the Turk. Although Vidal's engraving is after the Krichewsky version, our picture, which is painted more tightly by comparison, has a pentiment visible at the Turk's left elbow which would have originally been placed at a slightly higher angle. This might indicate that ours is the prime version and the Krichewsky *Amorous Proposal* a *répétition*.

In his discussion of this painting, Bordeaux writes, 'though the scene has a strong biblical overtone, it fails to yield its real theme with any precision'.[7] Indeed, there are resonances here to as far back as Le Moyne's early *Christ and the Woman of Samaria* (Cathedral of Sens) [FIG. 2], painted in 1720, where the svelte figures are posed around the well, and the Samarian woman's elegant costume is practically identical to the young woman's in the *Amorous Proposal*. And although there are neither camel, nor jug, nor gifts, our painting bears comparison with Piazzetta's *Rebecca at the Well* (Brera, Milan), where textual reference is subordinated to a painterly interest in costume and fabric, and where the sensuous and not entirely serious interplay between the protagonists is characteristic of genre painting as it would develop in the third and fourth decades of the eighteenth century. Alastair Laing has rather ingeniously connected the episode portrayed by Le Moyne to a scene from Tristan l'Hermite's tragedy, *Panthée* (1639), which the Regent adapted as a somewhat licentious opera.[8] It is unlikely that the simply dressed maiden, who might well be washing clothes, could be the Queen of Susa, held in noble captivity by Cyrus of Persia. And there is even less reason to see in the grizzled, lecherous Turk, Cyrus' childhood friend and companion, Araspas, who develops an overwhelming passion for Panthea. It is more satisfactory to interpret this genre scene as a precocious example of the vogue for *les Turqueries* that swept Parisian society in the 1720's.[9] Montesquieu's *Lettres Persanes* was published in 1721, the Ottoman ambassador, Mehemet Affendi, visited Paris in March of that year, and thereafter an enormous number of novels and plays would treat Turkish themes. Even if it was principally in decorative painting that *les Turqueries* dominated – and one thinks not only of Lajoue, but Lancret's *Amorous Turk* (Musée des Arts Decoratifs, Paris) and the series of *Foreign Hunts* for the Petits Appartements, Versailles – Le Moyne here showed himself open to the latest fashion, which he recast in a typically heroic and monumental manner.

A drawing of this subject, preparatory for Vidal's engraving, was sold at Christie's, London, 29 November 1983, no. 100, as *Abraham and Hagar*.[10]

Notes

[1] This entry relies a good deal on Alastair Laing's extremely interesting entry in *Art, Commerce, Scholarship: A window onto the Art World—Colnaghi 1760 to 1984*, London, 1984, p. 179, no. 57.

[2] *Catalogue de tableaux, dessins, estampes . . . provenans de la succession de feu M. Briard, Peintre du Roi*, Paris, 7 January 1778, no. 10.

[3] *European Masters of the eighteenth century*, exhib. cat., Royal Academy, London, 1954–5, no. 129, as Le Moyne.

[4] Laing, *op. cit.*, p. 180.

[5] P. Remy, *Catalogue de tableaux originaux des trois écoles . . . du cabinet de M. Pelt, Ecuyer et de celui de M. de XXX*, Paris, 21 February 1774, no. 105.

[6] J-L. Bordeaux, *op. cit.*, p. 101, no. 55.

[7] *Ibid.*, p. 102.

[8] Laing, *op. cit.*, p. 180.

[9] M. Roland Michel, 'Répresentations de l'exotisme dans la peinture en France de la première moitié du XVIIIe siècle', *Studies on Voltaire and the eighteenth century*, 154 (1976), pp. 1437–57.

[10] I owe this information to Marianne Roland Michel and Michel Gregor.

François Le Moyne

10 *Fecundity*

Oil on canvas, H.12$\frac{15}{16}$in. w.16$\frac{1}{16}$in.

Coll. Early provenance unknown; Private Collection, Switzerland; Stair Sainty Matthiesen.

FIG. 1 L. Cars, after Le Moyne's *Louis XV Giving Peace to Europe*

In 1729 François Le Moyne was commissioned to paint a huge *dessus de cheminée* for the Salon de Paix at Versailles; his subject was *Louis XV Giving Peace to Europe*. In this ambitious allegorical painting Louis XV hands an olive branch, symbol of peace, to a smiling Europe. Behind them we see the Temple of Janus with its doors firmly closed – note the medallion on the architrave – despite the efforts of Discord who tries to force them open. Minerva, seated upon a cloud to the top right of the composition, gestures to Mercury, symbol of Commerce, to ensure that Discord is prevented from upsetting the new-found peace. At the bottom right of the painting, a female figure, with a divine flame burning in her head, symbolizing Piety, offers the two infants, held by Fecundity, to Europe. These details are very clearly indicated in Laurent Cars' sanguine drawing after Le Moyne's painting [FIG. 1], preparatory to his engraving of 1730.[1]

Our painting is the *première pensée* for the figure of Fecundity who bears the two children. The passage was one of the most successful in the composition: Caylus wrote that the group was painted 'd'une couleur agréable et d'un pinceau séduisant'.[2] However, although contemporary commentators were in no doubt that this beautifully executed group represented the symbol of Fecundity – and this included such connoisseurs as Caylus, Mariette and Dezallier d'Argenville – recent authorities have confused the image as a depiction of Charity, which fails to identify the precise allusions Le Moyne intended.[3] For the painter combined two traditions in representing the symbol of Fecundity. Until the end of the seventeenth century Fecundity was most usually portrayed as a young woman crowned with strands of hemp: she might also be shown holding a nest of goldfinch, or with rabbits and chicken scratching around on the ground beneath her. She wears a garland of hemp, we are told, because this plant 'multiplies almost by itself and requires no tending, and so strong and tall does it grow that birds may perch upon it'.[4] A second tradition, which Ripa had found on ancient medals, has Fecundity 'a matron of pleasant countenance' caressing two children, and it is this motif that Le Moyne adapted so successfully in his allegorical painting to symbolize the continuity and growth of the French line. As the English editor of the late eighteenth-century edition of Ripa put it,

> The attitude of caressing two children expresses one of the greatest consolations of the married state, and indicates the happiness and delight that mankind enjoy in rearing their beloved offspring.[5]

Nor is Le Moyne's image confined to the realm of pure allegory. Both Caylus and Piganiol de la Force saw in the protective maternal figure and the young infants a reference to Louise-Elisabeth and Anne-Henriette, Louis XV's oldest children, born on 14 August 1727.[6]

It is difficult to trace the provenance of our *première pensée*, recognized as the finest of the many versions of this popular theme that are still extant. A similar painting, described as 'une belle et gracieuse étude finie' was owned by La Live de Jully, but the dimensions are some ten inches larger all round than our picture. Jean-Luc Bordeaux has connected our *Fecundity* with the *Charity* listed among Le Moyne's effects at the time of his death and valued at twelve-and-a-half livres, but as the inventory gives no indication of size such a connection remains tentative.[7]

10 François Le Moyne, *Fecundity*

FIG. 2 Le Moyne,
Study of Hands, Louvre

A beautiful drawing *aux trois crayons* of Fecundity's hands [FIG. 2], preparatory for the group as it appears in our picture and the final version, but incorrectly inscribed as 'étude de l'assomption' is at the Cabinet des Dessins, Louvre.[8]

Notes

[1] J-L. Bordeaux, *op. cit.*, p. 114, no. 76. The Laurent Cars drawing, H.22½in., W.17¼in., is in a private collection in New York.

[2] A. Fontaine, *Comte de Caylus: Vie d'Artistes du XVIIIe siècle*, Paris, 1910, p. 56.

[3] J-L. Bordeaux, *op. cit.*, pp. 114–15.

[4] C. Ripa, *Iconolgie, ou Explication nouvelle de plusieurs images, emblèmes et autres figures hyérogliphiques des vertus, des vices, des arts et des sciences*, Paris, 1644, p. 70.

[5] G. Richardson, ed., *Iconology, or a collection of Emblematical figures . . . selected from the emblematical representations of . . . Egyptians, Greeks and Romans and Cesar Ripa*, 2 vols, London, 1777–9, vol. 2, p. 71.

[6] Piganiol de la Force quoted in J-L. Bordeaux, *op. cit.*, p. 114; Fontaine, *op. cit.*, p. 56.

[7] J-L. Bordeaux, *op. cit.*, pp. 114–15 for a survey of the other versions.

[8] *Ibid.*, p. 163, no. 109.

Charles Coypel
Paris 1694–1752 Paris

A son of the First Painter of the King Antoine Coypel, grandson of Nöel and nephew of Nöel-Nicholas (his near contemporary), it is hardly surprising that this painter should have been received into the Academy at the age of twenty-one. A student of his father's, he did not make the pilgrimage to Rome but immediately embarked on a highly successful career as a history painter. His earliest major commission, a series of tapestry cartoons on the life of Don Quixote for the Gobelins factory, reflects his interest in literary subjects. He had a considerable reputation as a playwright and critic and the theatricality of his compositions became more exaggerated as his career progressed. In 1746 he actually withdrew his original Academy reception piece to substitute for it another painting (*Abraham Embracing his Son Isaac*), which demonstrated more successfully his dramatic style. Mariette criticized his deliberate attempts to avoid the portrayal of nature and his intellectual style was little appreciated by the succeeding generation of artists. His entry for the 1727 competition, *Andromeda* (Louvre), beautifully executed but displaying a stylized palette and artificial expressions, was much admired by some critics and was purchased by the King. However, Coypel was a wealthy man and his output was small, virtually ceasing after his appointment as First Painter, in 1747. He worked principally in oils but also executed some fine pastels and had considerable success as a portraitist. Thierry Lefrançois is preparing a monograph on the painter.

Charles Coypel

11 *Saint Piamun and her Mother in an Egyptian Village*

Oil on canvas, H.41⅞in. W.30½in.
Signed and dated, extreme lower left: *C. Coypel 1747.*

Coll. Oratory of Marie-Josèphe de Saxe, Dauphine, Versailles, 1747–1760; listed among 'les tableaux qui sont dans le Magasin' at the Surintendance des Bâtiments, Versailles,[1] 1760; 'Sujet de dévotion' in inventory of the Musée Spécial de l'Ecole Française,[2] 1797; given by the state to the Soeurs de la Charité à Versailles 'la même sainte encore enfant',[3] 1819 (?); later nineteenth-century provenance unknown; Stair Sainty Matthiesen.

In June 1747 the Dauphin Louis commissioned Charles Coypel to paint two pictures for the oratory of his second wife, Marie-Josèphe de Saxe – the mother of the future Louis XVI, Louis XVIII and Charles X – in her newly-decorated *appartement* at Versailles. Jacques-Ange Gabriel explained to the *Surintendant*, Le Normand de Tournehem, that the Dauphin 'veut dans les deux premiers (niches) une Sainte du désert peinte par M. Coypel et dans la niche du fond un tableau de l'Adoration du Roi par M. Vanloo'.[4] Just over a week later, Le Normand informed Coypel of this commission, requesting him to produce sketches for the Dauphin's approval, 'si vous avez le temps'.[5] By the middle of July, Coypel had the dimensions for his pictures, which were painted within the next four months, since Marie-Josèphe de Saxe was installed in her newly decorated ground-floor *appartement* by November of that year. With uncustomary efficiency, Coypel received payment for his two pictures in January 1748.[6]

Although the Dauphin imposed both the size and subject of Coypel's pendants, the actual episodes represented were the choice of the artist himself. *Saint Landrade Instructing the Young Women in her Care* [FIG. 1] (Private collection, Saint-Germain-en-Laye) refers to the story of a Frankish princess who set out in the company of widows and virgins 'de noble et d'illustre extraction' to build a monastery in the deserted region of Belise, in Belgium.[7]

Our painting treats an equally esoteric theme. It is the story of Saint Piamun, recounted by Palladius in his *Lausiac History* (XXX, 1–4), a fourth-century ascetic who lived with her mother in Upper Egypt and had the gift of prophecy. Palladius recounts that she prevented a neighboring village from overwhelming her own by asking God to make the attackers as 'immobile as columns'. However, Coypel bases his composition on the opening section of the story as it appeared in Arnauld d'Andilly's *Les Vies des Saints Pères des deserts et de quelques Saintes écrites par des pères de l'église . . .* (3 vols, Paris, 1733) – a popular anthology which had gone through several editions and which had already provided Coypel with the subjects for similar religious commissions from Marie Leczinska.[8] The passage relevant here may be quoted in full:

> And there was a virgin named Piamun who spent her days with her mother who was always with her in the house. She passed her time spinning flax and ate only in the evening, and God gave her the gift of prophecy.[9]

Thus, textual authority endows what appears at first as an unexceptionable, even banal, image with greater significance. The act of spinning is the essential attribute of the saint; the bare floorboards and the barred window in the background show the austerity of her existence. And the root vegetables, the bowl and pitcher in the foreground represent the meager sustenance she will take in the evening, once the sun has set. Coypel makes no reference to the more dramatic conclusion of the story: the mood is domestic, reflective and peaceful – entirely appropriate for the oratory of a

FIG. 1 C. Coypel, *Saint Landrade Instructing the Young Women in her Care*

11 Charles Coypel, *Saint Piamun and Her Mother in an Egyptian Village*

FIG. 2 C. Coypel,
Adoration of the Shepherds,
Musée des Beaux Arts, Dijon

devout sixteen-year-old princess. Yet the artist has followed the spirit as well as the letter of Arnauld d'Andilly's text. The Jansenist author had noted in an earlier edition to this anthology that he had 'omitted all signs of error or passion' in his translation in order that 'these stories and these lives, once purified, could be a source of illumination to those who could not read them in the original language'.[10] Coypel's image, with its precise allusions, allows the initiate to ponder the miracle performed through Saint Piamun's prayer while setting before him a vision of simple piety and abnegation.

The subdued tonal range of this painting – its sober ochres, browns, creams – and the assured handling – above all in the women's hands, and in the upper torso of the old woman – are characteristic of Coypel's late style. The wide-eyed innocence of Saint Piamun brings to mind *The Education of the Virgin* (J. B. Speed Art Museum, Louisville) and the *Virgin and Child* (Musée du Périgord, Périgueux), both painted a few years earlier. Thierry Lefrançois connected the *Saint Landrade* (the pendant to this painting) with Coypel's *Adoration of the Shepherds* [FIG. 2] (Musée des Beaux Arts, Dijon).[11] Not only does our picture show stylistic similarities in its richly painted draperies and confident impasto, but Coypel has used the figure of the old woman who stands at the far left of the Dijon picture to far greater effect as the mother, reading from the holy texts, in the *Saint Piamun*.

Notes

[1] This entry relies largely on the excellent notice in Th. Lefrançois, *Charles Coypel, Peintre du Roi (1694–1752)*, thèse de doctorat de IIIe cycle, Université de Paris-Sorbonne, 3 vols, Paris, 1983, vol. 2, pp. 592–7. I am extremely grateful to the author for allowing me to consult his doctoral thesis which is shortly to be published.

[2] Lefrançois, *op. cit.*, p. 592, citing Archives des Musées Nationaux, 35 DD 1, p. 19.

[3] L. Courajod, 'Objets d'art concédés en jouissance par la Restoration', *Nouvelles Archives de l'Art Français*, 1878, p. 377, where he notes that the Sainte Landrade 'et la même sainte encore enfant' were both given to the Soeurs de Charité at Versailles. It is most probable that he is referring here to the Saint Piamun.

[4] Lefrançois, *op. cit.*, p. 593. Gabriel's letter is dated 4 June 1747. Van Loo's picture was never executed.

[5] F. Engerand, 'Les commandes officielles de tableaux au XVIIIe siècle – Charles Coypel', *La Chronique des Arts et de la Curiosité*, 1896, pp. 344–5.

[6] Lefrançois, *op. cit.*, p. 594.

[7] *Ibid.*, p. 595.

[8] For example *Sainte Thaïs dans sa cellule* and *Sainte Azelle à la porte de son ermitage*, both painted in 1736 and now lost, were included in Arnauld d'Andilly's anthology.

[9] R. Arnauld d'Andilly, *Les Vies des Saints Pères des deserts et de quelques saintes écrites par des pères de l'église . . .*, 3 vols, Paris, 1733, vol. 2, p. 256.

[10] Quoted in A. Lucot, ed., *Palladius, Histoire Lausiaque*, Paris, 1912, p. lii.

[11] Lefrançois, *op. cit.*, p. 595.

Carle (Charles-André) Van Loo
Nice 1705–1765 Paris

The most famous painter of his generation, Carle Van Loo was the grandson of a Dutch painter who had ended his successful career in France. Nice, Van Loo's birthplace, was part of the Duchy of Savoy and the Prince of Savoy-Carignano sponsored his trip to Rome when he was in his early teens. Accompanied by his brother and first master, Jean-Baptiste Van Loo, he entered the studio of Benedetto Luti and also studied with the sculptor Le Gros before returning to Paris in 1719. Five years later he won the *Grand Prix* and returned to Italy in 1728. After working for the King of Sardinia in Turin (where he met his wife), he returned to Paris to be received into the Academy in 1735 with *Marsyas Punished by Apollo* (Louvre). Compared by Voltaire with Raphael, he successfully mastered the painting of history and religious subjects, portraits and genre scenes. He had a great success as a teacher at the *Ecole des Elèves Protégés* and was much patronized by the Court. In 1762 he was appointed *Premier Peintre du Roi*. A very fine technician and draftsman, he was a master of composition and gradually came to dominate French art after the death of Le Moyne. He was uniquely honored immediately after his death by his fellow painter, Dandré-Bardon, who wrote a biography and catalogue of his works. Marie-Catherine Sahut's catalogue to the 1977 Van Loo exhibition continues to be the major study of the painter.

Carle Van Loo

12 *Aeneas Carrying Anchises*

Oil on canvas, H.38½in. W.50in.

Coll. Early provenance unknown; sold Christies, London, 1 October 1976, no. 75 *Aeneas and Anchises*; Christies, London, 23 July 1982, no. 156, *Aeneas and Anchises* (unsold); Private Collection, London; Stair Sainty Matthiesen.

Our picture is one of three large-scale replicas of Carle Van Loo's magisterial *Aeneas Carrying Anchises*, painted in 1729, one year after the twenty-three-year-old student had arrived in Rome. The dramatic moment when Anchises, father of Aeneas, submits to the wishes of the gods and prepares to leave Troy with his family in order to maintain his line, forms the climax of the second book of the *Aeneid*. We see Virgil's hero, Aeneas, clad in Trojan armor, carrying his aged father on his back, while his young son, Ascanius, clutches Aeneas' red-brown cloak and looks around fearfully at the city of Troy in flames. Anchises receives a statuette of Minerva, one of the household gods, from Creusa, daughter of Priam, King of Troy – the wife of Aeneas, who is not destined to make the journey with them.

FIG. 1 Van Loo, *Aeneas Carrying Anchises*, Louvre

Van Loo's heroic picture, with its rich hues and dramatic lighting, brought the young painter great fame. Engraved shortly after he returned to France, the *Aeneas Carrying Anchises* [FIG. 1] entered the pioneering collection of French painting formed by Ange-Laurent de La Live de Jully, and was finally acquired by the Crown in 1777, after passing through the prestigious collection of the Prince de Conti.[1]

The replica exhibited here is painted with great assurance and is faithful to the original in all areas except for the foreground steps which are less confidently painted. Unlike the replicas at the Musée des Beaux Arts, Angers, and the Musée Lambinet, Versailles – which we have only been able to study through photographs – the expressions of both Creusa and Anchises are rendered with the same dramatic intensity that is found in the Louvre's painting. The figure of Creusa – wide-eyed, with her mouth slightly gaping in the Angers replica – has all the tightness of the original in ours. Similarly, the tilt of Anchises' head, his pursed lips and the modelling of his upper torso are most like the first version in our painting.

Unlike François Le Moyne, Van Loo rarely duplicated successful compositions: on the contrary, he was more likely to destroy work that fell short of his expectations.[2] Nor are there contemporary references to large-scale replicas of *Aeneas Carrying Anchises* of the high quality of our painting. In his annotations to Louis-Michel Van Loo's sale catalogue – the portraitist owned the Louvre *Aeneas* for one year (1770–1) – Gabriel de Saint Aubin jotted down 'la copie du neveu, 162 Salatin (?)', which suggests that Louis-Michel may have worked on one of the replicas.[3] The only other reference to a second version of the *Aeneas* is to be found in an evaluation of pictures belonging to a certain Baron Knyphausen, which has been dated to c. 1768, and whose *Fuite d'Enée* was estimated at 120 livres.[4] In both cases these references are too elliptical to be connected with any of the three extant replicas.

In producing this precocious and heroic history painting, Van Loo was surely inspired by pictures of the same story that he could have seen and studied in Rome. Marie-Catherine Sahut proposed Barocci's *Aeneas' Flight from Troy* [FIG. 2], in the Galleria Borghese since the early seventeenth century, as a source for Van Loo's picture – and Barocci is an artist who particularly marked the young French painter.[5] Although Roman influences, both ancient (Raphael, Bernini, Barocci) and modern (Placido

12 Carle Van Loo, *Aeneas Carrying Anchises*

FIG. 2 F. Barocci, *Aeneas' Flight from Troy*, Galeria Borghese, Rome

FIG. 3 P. Lepautre, *Aeneas Carrying Anchises*, Tuileries, Paris

Constanzi) cannot be questioned, the pervasiveness of the image of Aeneas and Anchises in Paris, and its political implications for the Regency have received less attention. Not only was Pierre Lepautre's sculpted group of *Aeneas Carrying Anchises* [FIG. 3] moved from Marly to the Tuileries in 1718 (where it has remained ever since), but it was at precisely this time that Antoine Coypel, Premier Peintre du Roi, painted the *Galerie d'Enée* for the Regent: his *Aeneas Carrying Anchises* (Musée Fabre, Montpellier) was not without significance for the young Van Loo.[6] And it was in the Orléans collection that Van Loo would have seen the first version of Barocci's *Flight from Troy*, now lost, acquired by the Regent in 1721.[7] The association between Augustan Rome and Louis XIV's France had been made explicit in the dedication of the most popular French translation of the *Aeneid* – a new edition appeared in 1719. This showed, as its frontispiece, an anonymous engraving of the central group of Barocci's *Aeneas* (which Van Loo followed most closely). It was entirely fitting, wrote the translator,

> that the most heroic work of Antiquity, itself dedicated to the most august of the Caesars, should receive the protection of a Monarch who revived the splendor of the Caesars and the virtuousness of Heroes.[8]

The Regency, by extension, would maintain and continue the glorious achievements of Augustus' heir. The young Van Loo would have had ample opportunity to study these heroic images and ponder their political implications before setting off for Rome in 1728.

Notes

[1] M-C. Sahut and P. Rosenberg, *Carle Van Loo, 1705–65*, exhib. cat., Nice, Clermont-Ferrand, Nancy, 1977, pp. 27–8, no. 7.

[2] Referring to this, Dandré-Bardon noted 'there are a great number of his finest compositions which have completely disappeared', M. F. Dandré-Bardon, *Vie de Carle Van Loo*, Paris, 1765, p. 36.

[3] M-C. Sahut, *op. cit.*, p. 28.

[4] M. de Fróville, 'Estimation de tableaux au XVIIIe siècle', *NAAF*, 3e série, 4 (1888), p. 64.

[5] H. Olsen, *Federico Barocci*, Copenhagen, 1962, pp. 180–1.

[6] F. Souchal, *French Sculptors of the seventeenth and eighteenth centuries*, 2 vols, Oxford, 1977–81, vol. 2, p. 377. For Coypel's Aeneas pictures, A. Schnapper, 'Antoine Coypel: La Galerie d'Enée au Palais Royal', *Revue de l'Art*, 5 (1969), pp. 38–42.

[7] Olsen, *op. cit.*, pp. 180–1.

[8] J. Renaud de Segrais, *Traduction de l'Enéide de Virgile*, 2 vols, Lyon, 1719, vol. 1, p. iii.

Carle Van Loo

13 *Noli Me Tangere*

Oil on canvas, H.26⅝in. W.20⅛in.

Coll. Cayeux (?), 1735–1769; sold Paris, Dec. 1769/Jan. 1770, no. 41, 600 livres; Coll. Vassal de Saint-Hubert, 1774; sold Paris, 17–21 Jan. 1774, no. 98, 1,600 livres to Le Brun; Coll. Dulac and Lachaise, 1778; sold Paris, 30 Nov. 1778, no. 211, 300 livres to Lenglier; Coll. P. E. Moitte, 1780; sold Paris, 14 Nov. 1780, no. 135; nineteenth-century provenance unknown; Richard Rush collection, 1968–1974 (on loan to Finch College Museum); Private Coll., New York, 1974–1983; Stair Sainty Matthiesen; acquired by the New Orleans Museum of Art, Apr. 1983.[1]

Lent by the New Orleans Museum of Art.

Exhibition: Orléans, Musée des Beaux Arts, *Peintures françaises du Museum of Art de la Nouvelle Orléans*, 9 May–15 September 1984, cat. no. 6, pp. 28–9.

FIG. 1 Van Loo, *Saint John the Baptist*, Galerie Pardo, Paris

According to Van Loo's first biographer, the history painter and author Michel-François Dandré-Bardon (1700–83), the *Noli Me Tangere* was painted in 1735, one year after Van Loo returned to Paris following a seven-year stay in Italy and the year in which he was made a full member of the Academy with his *Apollo Flaying Marsyas* (Ecole des Beaux-Arts, Paris). Our painting and its pendant, *Saint John the Baptist* (Galerie Pardo, Paris) [FIG. 1]), were probably painted for the sculptor and collector of French painting, Philippe Cayeux (1688–1769).[2] Cayeux's collection, consisting almost exclusively of religious works by eighteenth-century French artists, included four canvases by Van Loo, among which was the early student piece, the *Blinding of the Sodomites*, known only through Saint Aubin's illustration to the Cayeux sale catalogue.[3] Given that the sculptor had started collecting as early as 1707 and that he was a friend of the 'greater number of artists of his day' – he had worked on the *Fontaine de Grenelle* and would design frames for Joseph Vernet – it is not unlikely that he commissioned this pair of *cabinet* pictures directly from Van Loo, who would have just returned to Paris.[4] In any case, both pictures are documented as in Cayeux's collection from the mid-1760's.[5]

Speaking of the various manners in which Van Loo excelled, Dandré-Bardon commented that the artist's *cabinet* pictures were executed 'avec toute la finesse et tout le précieux qu'elle est susceptible' ('with the greatest care and delicacy imaginable').[6] This is particularly true of both the *Noli Me Tangere* and the *Saint John the Baptist* – among Van Loo's earliest documented *cabinet* paintings. Our picture is tightly drawn and carefully modelled, and the figure of Christ the gardener striding forward is painted with great sureness of touch. It recalls the figure of Apollo, though in reverse, from the *Apollo Flaying Marsyas* painted that same year.

This early, Italianate work, much indebted to both Correggio and Guido, may also have been inspired by Barocci's painting of the same subject, the smaller version of which Van Loo could have seen in Florence.[7] Typically, Van Loo has treated the story of Christ before the Magdalene (John:20:17) quite traditionally. The attributes of the gardener and the formerly luxurious Magdalene are conventional, as are the poses both figures adopt. Yet the creation of a mood of understated piety that is not without a sensuous resonance is an astonishing achievement in a comparatively early work.

Van Loo would return to the theme of the Magdalene in an exquisite drawing, done slightly later than the painting, and acquired by Carl

FIG. 2 Van Loo,
Magdalene,
Nationalmuseum,
Stockholm

Gustav Tessin between 1739 and 1741 [FIG. 2] (Nationalmuseum, Stockholm).[8] In both painting and drawing the Magdalene's impassioned faith is given precedence over her worldly beauty and sumptuous apparel.

Our painting was engraved by Salvador Carmona in 1755. A large-scale painted copy, after the engraving and so with the figures in reverse, is to be found at the church of Saint-Louis-en-l'Ile, Paris.[9]

Notes

[1] Provenance established by M-C. Sahut, *op. cit.*, p. 93, no. 204. See also E. Caraco, 'New Acquisitions: Paintings by eighteenth-century French Masters', *Arts Quarterly*, October–December 1983, pp. 10–13.

[2] M-F. Dandré-Bardon, *Vie de Carle Van Loo*, Paris, 1765, p. 63 'chez M. Cayeu, [*sic*]'.

[3] M-C. Sahut, *op. cit.*, p. 90, no. 189. Saint Aubin's illustrated catalogue is in the Musée du Petit Palais, Paris.

[4] P. Remy, *Catalogue raisonné des tableaux, bronzes, terres cuites . . . qui composent le cabinet de feu M. Cayeux, sculpteur, ancien officier de l'Académie de Saint Luc*, Paris, 1770, 'Avertissement'. For a short notice on Cayeux, see U. Thieme and F. Becker, *Allgemeines Lexicon der bildenden Künstler*, 37 vols, Leipzig, 1907–50, vol. 6, p. 240

[5] The pictures are mentioned in Dandré-Bardon's manuscript notes, 'Liste des principaux ouvrages de Carle Van Loo', in *Bibl. Nat. Manuscrits*, Fonds Français, 13081, *Recueil des Manuscrits divers*, fol. 259.

[6] Dandré-Bardon, *op. cit.*, p. 27.

[7] Reproduced H. Olsen, *Federico Barocci*, Copenhagen, 1962, plate 57.

[8] M-C. Sahut, *op. cit*, p. 118, no. 345.

[9] This copy, incorrectly dated to the end of the seventeenth century, is listed in the *Inventaire général des richesses d'Art en France, Paris: Monuments religieux*, vol. 3, 1901, p. 343.

13 Carle Van Loo, *Noli Me Tangere*

Carle Van Loo

14 *The Annunciation*

Oil on canvas, H.32½in. w.16in.
Signed, lower center: *Carle Van Loo.*

Coll. Early provenance unknown; sale, Sotheby, London, 9 July 1975, no. 103; Private Collection, New York; Stair Sainty Matthiesen.

At the Salon of 1746 Carle Van Loo exhibited three large vertical canvases representing scenes from the life of the Virgin and painted for the *Chapelle de la Vierge*, the oldest and grandest chapel of the Saint-Sulpice church. A fourth painting, the *Adoration of the Shepherds*, was *in situ* by 1748.[1] 'Les quatres tableaux de M. Vanlo [*sic*] ne sont pas un des moindres ornamens de cette chapelle' wrote the *amateur* and friend of Greuze and Pigalle, the abbé Gougenot.[2] Nor was this empty praise, since these four pictures were probably the last to be commissioned by Jean-Baptiste Languet de Gergy (1675–1750), the dynamic curé of Saint-Sulpice, who had dedicated some twenty years to

> the embellishment of this chapel, wishing to bring it to a state of beauty and perfection that it had not known since the time it was built.[3]

Servandoni had redesigned the interior in 1729; François Le Moyne was responsible for painting the huge cupola with scenes from the Assumption of the Virgin (1731–2); Michel-Ange Slodtz and Edme Bouchardon both participated in the decoration of the main altar.[4]

Our sketch is a preliminary study for the *Annunciation* [FIG.1], one of the three pictures shown at the Salon of 1746. With its remarkable pearly tonality, its cool, refined blues, greys and greens, and its loose flowing, undulating draperies, it achieves a quietude and harmony that certain critics found missing from the finished work. La Font de Saint-Yenne, full of praise for the dignity and humility with which the Virgin was portrayed, was less satisfied with the stiffness of the archangel and the heaviness of both figures' robes. Gougenot criticized the wooden draperies and also took exception to the strained posture of the kneeling Virgin.[5]

While the final picture follows the sketch quite closely, there are important differences. The shaft of light that illuminates the descending Archangel and leads the eye to the kneeling Mary in the sketch, enters from a window to the right in the finished picture, where it is also more diffuse, thus accentuating the narrowness of this large composition. Whereas the Archangel stands on a cloud in the full-scale work, he is kneeling in the sketch where the clouds are used more effectively to bring the two figures together: a device Gougenot specifically recommended in his review of the finished picture. The bottom left of the composition, empty in the final work, is blocked in by a chair and a book in the sketch, which squares off the image with greater balance.

A beautiful wash drawing of the subject, signed but not dated, and in the Weimar Museum [FIG.2], may be connected with the Saint-Sulpice *Annunciation*.[6] In the drawing the figures are shown in reverse of our sketch and the interior is far more carefully depicted. However, there may be a relation between drawing and sketch, since we can see in the latter an unfinished wing, painted in grey in the top right-hand corner. This would suggest that Van Loo initially grouped his figures as in the Weimar drawing, where the wing of the angel, who enters from the right, occupies a similar space.

In his pioneering study of religious art after the Council of Trent, Emile Mâle argued that the changes in the iconography of the Annunciation were revealing of a new aggressive spirituality, characteristic of the Counter Reformation. Whereas, in the Middle Ages and the Renaissance, the

FIG. 1 Van Loo, *Annunciation*, Church of Saint-Sulpice, Paris

FIG. 2 Van Loo, *Annunciation*, Weimar Museum

14 Carle Van Loo, *The Annunciation*

Annunciation was treated with a 'profoundly touching intimacy', pictorial changes from the late sixteenth century onward would serve to emphasize the grandiose and the declamatory:

> The sky has now overwhelmed the cell in which the Virgin is at prayer, and the angel, carrying a lily, enters the room kneeling on a cloud. Shafts of light, at once mysterious and luminous, obliterate the bed, the interior and the walls – in a word, everything that brings to mind the realities of everyday life.[7]

Mâle could almost be describing Van Loo's *Annunication*, since Carle's treatment of the theme was entirely traditional. Yet in his gently understated interpretation of the subject, Van Loo achieves a quality of sweet and direct grace, characteristic of his greatest religious paintings, and reinvests this momentous scene with a humane and intimate dimension.

Notes

[1] M-C. Sahut, *op. cit.*, p. 60, nos. 100–3.

[2] (L. Gougenot), *Lettre sur la peinture, sculpture et architecture, à M . . .*, 1748, p. 38.

[3] Archives de Saint-Sulpice, *Ms 98*, Simmonet, *Le Nouveau Temple de Salomon ou description historique de l'église paroissiale de Saint-Sulpice*, fol. 222. I am grateful to the librarian of the Saint-Sulpice seminary for access to this unpublished manuscript.

[4] M. Dumolin and G. Outardel, *Les Eglises de France*, Paris, 1936, pp. 166–7.

[5] Gougenot, *op. cit.*, p. 39; La Font de Saint-Yenne, *Réflexions sur quelques causes de l'état present de la peinture en France*, La Haye, 1747, pp. 50–1.

[6] M-C. Sahut, *op. cit.*, p. 128, no. 381.

[7] E. Mâle, *L'Art religieux de la fin du XVIe siècle, du XVIIe et du XVIIIe siècle*, Paris, 1951, pp. 239–40.

François Boucher
Paris 1703–1770 Paris

Of all the 'First Painters of the King', none has achieved a greater and more lasting fame than Boucher. Certainly no artist of his time rivalled his success. Working first in the studio of J-Fr. Cars, as an engraver, Boucher also entered Le Moyne's *atelier* around 1720 and won the *Premier Prix* with his *Evilmerodach Delivering Joachim* (whereabouts unknown) three years later. He too left for Rome independently, spending between 1727 and 1731 in Italy, and gaining full membership of the Academy in 1734 with his *Rinaldo and Armida* (Louvre), which bears the influence of his former teacher, Le Moyne. However, by the late 1730's Boucher's style evolved into a more personal language, suited above all to large-scale decorative painting – both for Parisian clients and tapestry manufacturers – but equally at ease with smaller-scale *cabinet* pictures (*Diana Resting*, Louvre) and even genre painting (*The Luncheon*, Louvre). Enormously successful and well patronized, his output was prodigious. He worked for numerous Royal and princely households – in the 1750's he was the favored painter of the Marquise de Pompadour – as well as the Beauvais and Gobelins tapestry factories, taking over the direction of the latter in 1755. He designed stage sets for the theater and the opera, as well as providing models for the Sèvres porcelain factory. Not since Le Brun had a single French artist exercised such a monopoly over the imagery of a particular society.

Despite a critical reaction against his work that was formulated during his lifetime and continued unabated until well into the following century, Boucher's idyllic and pastoral world, with only the slightest connection to 'reality', found favor with private patrons throughout his career. Ironically his decorative style was vindicated in the second commission for Choisy (1766), made after Louis XV had rejected Cochin's grandiose and ill-fated attempt to imbue decorative painting with a greater didactic content. Ananoff's catalogue raisonné has been the standard reference book on Boucher for almost a decade, but much new material is expected from Alastair Laing's catalogue for the forthcoming Boucher exhibition in New York, Detroit and Paris, 1986.

François Boucher

15 *Leda and the Swan*

Oil on canvas, H.23⅜in. W.29¼in.
Signed right center on rock: *f. Boucher*.

Coll. Harenc de Presle, sold Paris, 16–24 April 1792, no. 59 (presumably bought in); coll. Harenc de Presle, sold Paris II Floréal an III (30 April 1795), no. 67, 1,200 livres to Le Brun; coll. Countess of Pembroke, Rome (?); coll. Theodore Patureau, sold privately to Dr Lombard, Liège; coll. comte d'Hane de Steenhuyse et de Leeuwergehm, sold Paris, 27 March 1860, no. 3, 3,000 francs; coll. Carlton Gates, sold New York, 21 December 1876, no. 480; coll. Prof. Paolo Paolini, sold New York (American Art Galleries), 11 December 1924, no. 112; coll. George F. Harding Museum, Chicago, consigned to Sotheby's, New York, 2 December 1976, no. 153, sale cancelled by the State of Illinois; Sotheby's, New York, 6 June 1985, no. 147 (as 'Studio of François Boucher');[1] Stair Sainty Matthiesen.

Exhibition: Paris, Salon of 1742, no. 21 bis.

Among the paintings and sketches Boucher submitted to the Salon of 1742 were two cabinet pictures of mythological subjects – *Diana Resting* (Louvre) and *Leda and the Swan* – both painted with great refinement and delicacy and in a finished manner appropriate to their modest scale. *Leda and the Swan* is best known from the version commissioned by Count Carl Gustaf Tessin and shipped to Sweden in June 1742, where it has remained ever since [FIG. 1]. As it is clear that this picture could not have appeared at the Paris Salon, which opened on 25 August (the King's Feast Day), the *Leda and the Swan*, listed as number '21 bis' in the Salon *livret*, has been considered lost until very recently.[2]

This painting, the 'Paris' *Leda*, was engraved by the English engraver William Wynne Ryland (1732–85) in 1758 and an advertisement for it appeared in the *Mercure* in August of that year.[3] The engraving differs from the Stockholm *Leda* in the patterning of the drapery that falls between Leda and her companion, as well as in details in the shrubbery to their right. The engraving, but not the notice in the *Mercure*, further stipulated that this version of Boucher's *Leda and the Swan* was 'tiré du cabinet de M. de Prele [*sic*]'.[4]

It is this picture – the 1742 Salon entry and the engraved painting listed in the catalogue of 'M. Aranc [*sic*] de Presle' – that we are showing here, a major discovery since it is not only the 'lost' Salon painting, but is also the prime version of the subject. The freer style in which it is painted – note the slightly softer contours of the faces of Leda and her companion – as well as the pentiments in the drapery and in the positioning of Leda's left

FIG. 1 Boucher, *Leda and the Swan*, Nationalmuseum, Stockholm

15 François Boucher, *Leda and the Swan*

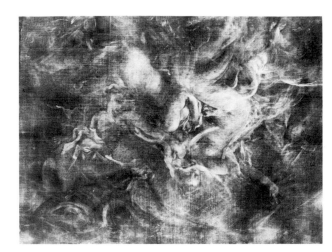

FIG. 2
X-ray (upside down)
Boucher,
Leda and the Swan

leg and the swan's neck – would already suggest that the Salon painting was executed before the Stockholm *Leda*. But recent X-ray photographs of the composition offer even more conclusive evidence that this is the prime version. For when our painting is turned upside down, the X-ray reveals that Boucher first treated the theme more traditionally, showing Leda reclining voluptuously with the long-necked swan imposing himself against her breast [FIG. 2]. Boucher must have abandoned this idea early on, turned the canvas around, and started again. The clearly legible X-ray provides a fascinating insight into his working method.

The major differences follow those noted for the engraving. In the Stockholm picture the stripes of the brocade that is held by Leda's companion are clearly indicated through the folds: in our painting the regularity of the pattern is interrupted as the drapery falls to the ground. Secondly, the silvery tufts of grass on the hillock at the right of our picture do not appear in the Stockholm version.

Our painting was first owned by the important collector, François-Michel Harenc de Presle (1710–1802), whose collection 'des trois écoles' was ranked eighth in Paris by Thiéry in 1784.[5]. We know that he refurbished his town house on the Rue du Sentier in the late 1750's and it is possible that he also began forming his small but choice picture cabinet at this time. Boucher's *Leda and the Swan* is documented as in his collection from August 1758. The picture is recorded as hanging in the *petit cabinet* along-side cabinet pictures by Breughel and Palamedesz some twenty-eight years later when Thiéry, in his long description of Harenc de Presle's collection, praised Boucher's painting as 'de son meilleur temps'.[6]

François-Michel Harenc de Presle, from a Protestant banking family which had converted after the Edict of Nantes, purchased the office of *Secrétaire du Roi* in 1744, and although he remained attached to financial circles in Paris – his brother-in-law was one of the directors of the East India Company – he was not an active banker as had been his forebears. He seems to have withdrawn from commerce and is simply described as 'écuyer' in the documents that we have discovered, probably maintaining an elegant and aristocratic style of living as befitted a wealthy *anobli* who had acquired hereditary nobility with the purchase of this expensive office.[7]

Jean-Baptiste-Pierre Lebrun, who managed his first estate sale in April 1792, wrote that he was selling off his collection because of impending blindness.[8] When the collection came onto the market a second time, exactly three years later, Joseph-Alexandre Lebrun (1755–1802) – the younger brother of the more famous picture dealer – gave no reason for the sale. It is likely that, by this time, the loss of Harenc de Presle's fortune compelled him to sell off his paintings and furniture.

On his death, seven years later (19 March 1802), no paintings of any value were listed among his effects, whose combined value was estimated at under 20,000 livres.[9] Nonetheless it is interesting to note a certain consist-

FIG. 3 C. Natoire, *Leda and the Swan*
J. P. Morgan Library

FIG. 4 Boucher, *Odalisque*,
Louvre

ency of taste among the grandees of the ancien régime – the Queen of Sweden and a first generation noble owning versions of the same erotic cabinet painting – especially since it was the banker's son who purchased the prime version.

Describing Ryland's print after our painting, the *Mercure* recommended Boucher's *Leda* for its novel interpretation of the subject ('la nouveauté de la disposition du sujet') as well as the charm of his draughtsmanship (l'agrément du dessin').[10] Indeed, Boucher's instincts are unerringly pictorial: he is less concerned with textual fidelity, as a comparison between the unfinished first idea and the final versions shows. Nowhere, in the various accounts of Jupiter's seduction of Leda, wife of King Tydnareus of Sparta – an amorous encounter that would produce Castor and Pollux, Helen and Clytaemnestra – and there allusions to a second female of the beauty of Leda herself. Furthermore, in his *Leda and the Swan*, Boucher plays down the impending seduction – unlike his engraved drawings of the subject there is no reference to Cupid.[11] Nor does his craning swan invoke the menacing lust of the most powerful of the gods as does Natoire's beautiful picture of the same subject [FIG. 3], which in other ways is quite similar to Boucher's. The striped brocade, the leafy vegetation, Leda's foot resting on the water, are elements common to both paintings. Instead Boucher inserts a recumbent nude that appears countless times in his *oeuvre*: notably in the *Odalisque* [FIG. 4] (Louvre) and the *Education of Love* (Charlottenburg, Berlin), the latter commissioned by Frederick the Great and painted within one year of *Leda and the Swan*.[12] By the addition of a second female figure Boucher produces a sumptuous pyramid of white flesh and luxurious raiment where the overtly erotic is tempered by a pastoral intimacy midway between the Euphrates and the Opéra Comique.

Notes

[1] I am greatly indebted to Alastair Laing who allowed me to see his entry on the Stockholm *Leda* for the forthcoming Boucher exhibition. I am following the provenance he established for the Salon painting.

[2] Laing's entry would have been the first to make the connection between our painting and the *Leda* exhibited in 1742. In the recent Boucher exhibition at the City Art Museum, Manchester, the Salon picture was noted for the first time as having 'disappeared', *François Boucher: Paintings, Drawings and Prints from the Nationalmuseum, Stockholm*, exhib. cat., Manchester, 1984, P. 2, p. 17.

[3] *Mercure de France*, Aoust 1758, p. 157.

[4] P. Jean-Richard, *L'Oeuvre gravé de François Boucher*, Paris, 1978, p. 371, no. 1539.

[5] L.-V. Thiéry, *Almanach du voyageur à Paris*, Paris, 1784, p. 158.

[6] *Idem, Guide des amateurs et des étrangers à Paris*, 2 vols, Paris, 1787, vol. 1, p. 448.

[7] A. N., *Minutier Central*, V/886, *Inventaire après décès*, François Michel Harenc de Presle, 5 Germinal an X (26 March 1802).

[8] J. B. P. Lebrun, *Catalogue d'objets rares et précieux en tout genre formant le Cabinet de M. Aranc de Presle*, Paris, 1792, 'Avertissement'.

[9] *Inventaire après décès, op. cit.*

[10] *Mercure, op. cit.*

[11] Jean-Richard, *op. cit.*, nos. 820 and 1395.

[12] Ananoff, *op. cit.*, nos. 204, 264 and 285.

François Boucher

16 *Vulcan Presenting Arms to Venus for Aeneas*

Oil on canvas, H.16$\frac{3}{15}$in. W.17$\frac{7}{8}$in.
Signed bottom right: *f. Boucher, 1756.*

Coll. Marquis de Marigny, sold Paris, 18 March–6 April 1782, no. 24,
300 livres to Remy (with Pierre's *Rape of Europa*); coll. Beaujon, sold
Paris, 25 April 1787, no. 203, 216 livres (with Pierre's *Rape of Europa*);
Private Collection, Washington; nineteenth-century provenance unknown;
Newhouse Galleries, New York; Sterling and Francine Clark Art Institute,
Williamstown, Massachusetts (acquired 1983).

Lent by the Sterling and Francine Clark Art Institute, Williamstown,
Massachusetts.

Exhibition: Museum of Fine Arts, Springfield, Massachusetts, *Masterpieces by François Boucher from New England Collections*, April–June
1984 (no catalogue).

In November 1755 the Marquis de Marigny sought Royal permission for a
new series of tapestry cartoons for the Gobelins factory, 'pour ranimer la
manufacture'.[1] By the following year Marigny had in fact commissioned
the four leading history painters in France – all of whom would one day
hold office as *Premier Peintre* – to produce sketches for a series devoted to
the loves of the gods. Van Loo was to paint *Neptune and Amymone* (Musée
Cheret, Nice), Boucher, *Venus and Vulcan* (Louvre), Pierre, *The Rape of
Europa* (formerly Arras, see entry 18), and Vien, *A Sacrifice to Ceres*
(Musée des Beaux Arts, Grenoble). It was only in May 1757 that Louis XV
gave his approval for the *Loves of the Gods* tapestry, even though the
sketches had been executed in 1756, and presumably on Marigny's orders.
Indeed, the first set was specifically intended as a gift for the Marquis de
Marigny himself, since, as the official *brevet* noted, 'de tous temps le Roi
accorde une tenture au Directeur des Bâtiments'.[2]

The ten-feet-square cartoons were exhibited in the Salon of 1757 alongside
the even larger history paintings commissioned by Frederick the Great
(see entry 19). Boucher's *Forge of Vulcan* [FIG. 1] was late in arriving,
though, when it finally appeared, it was hailed by Salon critics as the
artist's masterpiece. For once, fears that Boucher's facility and success
were leading younger artists astray were subdued in favor of unanimous
praise for the sheer brilliance with which he had interpreted this traditional theme. The harmony and balance of the various groups set against
the swirling dynamism of the composition achieved 'the most ingenious

FIG. 1 Boucher, *Forge of Vulcan*,
Louvre

16 François Boucher, *Vulcan Presenting Arms to Venus for Aeneas* (This picture will not be shown at Columbus)

FIG. 2 Boucher, *Vulcan Presenting Arms to Venus*, Musée des Arts Décoratifs, Paris

pictorial unity ('enchaînement de composition'), so coherent that no one part can be taken away'.[3] The subtle range of pinks, blues and greens, and the careful arrangement of light and shadow, were ample proof of Boucher's technical excellence. He was the painter 'who had excelled in more aspects of his art than any of his contemporaries'.[4]

The Clark's *Vulcan Presenting Arms to Venus for Aeneas*, the *première pensée* for the Louvre's *Forge of Vulcan*, was painted in 1756 and possibly presented for official approval before the large-scale version could be executed.[5] The sketch remained in Marigny's possession and appeared in his sale of April 1782, where it was aptly described as 'plein d'esprit et de feu'. There are important differences between the sketch and the finished painting. In the sketch we see Vulcan's anvil and the Cyclops at work at the far right of the composition. Immediately behind Vulcan one of his attendants has just arrived with Aeneas' breastplate. Both these elements are suppressed in the final version. In the place of the anvil we see the head and shoulders of one of Vulcan's workers as he climbs out of the underground forge. And, seated on a cloud just above Vulcan's head, two putti play with Aeneas' plumed helmet.

This bravura sketch, with its short, stabbing strokes of creams, pinks and blues is a marvellous example of how assured and instinctive was Boucher's narrative sense. In the most economic way he lays out a composition that stretches over four planes, with clouds, putti and white doves maintaining a sort of perpetual motion, which is furthermore enhanced by the spirited and abbreviated manner in which the paint is applied. The artist's genius consisted in preserving this dynamism and energy in the finished version on a scale that might have been expected to neutralise the movement and excitement of the *première pensée*.

A slightly smaller grisaille sketch of the same composition as the Clark picture is in the Musée des Arts Decoratifs, Paris [FIG. 2].[6] There is a copy of the subject, but without the anvil, in the Yale University Art Gallery.

Notes

[1] F. Engerand, *Inventaire des tableaux commandés et achetés par la direction des Bâtiments du Roi (1709–92)*, Paris, 1901, p. 52.

[2] M. Fenaille, *Etat général des Tapisseries de la Manufacture des Gobelins. Dixhuitième Siècle : deuxième partie, 1737–94*, Paris, 1907, p. 189.

[3] Fréron in l'Année Littéraire, quoted in A. Ananoff, *François Boucher*, 2 vols, Lausanne, 1976, vol. 1, p. 79.

[4] (?) Renou, in *Extrait des observations sur la physique et les arts*, quoted in Ananoff, *op. cit.*, vol. 1, p. 78.

[5] Marigny had assured the king that the tapestries would only be woven once 'Votre Majesté' aurait agréé les dessins et les esquisses', Engerand, *op. cit.*, p. 52.

[6] Ananoff, *op. cit.*, vol. 2, no. 479 bis.

Jean-Baptiste-Marie Pierre
Paris 1714–1789 Paris

Overshadowed by Boucher, and a man whose difficult personality made him unpopular during his lifetime, Pierre and his work have only recently been rehabilitated. Born into a wealthy family, Pierre studied first with Natoire, winning the *Grand Prix* in 1734 at the age of twenty. In Rome from 1735 to 1740, little is known of his work during this time when the Academy was under the direction first of Vleughels and then De Troy. Received into the Academy in 1742 with *Diomedes Slain by Hercules* (Montpellier), he exhibited regularly at the Salon until 1751, then at the Salons of 1761 and 1769. He succeeded Boucher as First Painter in 1770 and assumed the Directorship of the Academy, after which he virtually abandoned painting. His early history paintings, such as the *Death of Harmonia* (Metropolitan, New York), exhibit a brilliant technique and mastery of composition which he lost in some of his later works. His delicate palette, always a little colder than Boucher's, and his more controlled style were particularly suited to the large-scale religious works which can be counted as among his most notable achievements. The decorative *bambochades* which he painted from the mid-1740's had considerable success with the public but did not endear him to the critics. As First Painter he was, with d'Angiviller, the most influential figure in artistic life in France during the reign of Louis XVI. Monique Halbout's unpublished dissertation is the only substantial recent study of the artist.

Jean-Baptiste-Marie Pierre

17 *The Forge of Vulcan*

Oil on canvas: $22\frac{1}{4}$in × $23\frac{1}{4}$in.; painted circular: $22\frac{1}{4}$in. diameter.

Coll. Early provenance unknown; sale, Christie's, London, 11 February 1983, no. 14, as Roman School; Stair Sainty Matthiesen.

The *Forge of Vulcan* is a preliminary version of a lost painting known today from Louis-Simon Lempereur's engraving of 1762 which was exhibited in the Salon of 1763 and dedicated to the Marquis de Marigny [FIG. 1].[1] It represents a theme painted countless times during the eighteenth century: the story of Venus requesting arms for Aeneas, told in the eighth book of the *Aeneid* (verses 370–453). Vulcan, seduced by his godly spouse and persuaded to make arms for the brave warrior, leaves Venus' bedchamber in the middle of the night to return to his forge. There, with his assistants, the Cyclops, he creates a shield capable of withstanding 'every missile of Latium'.[2] It is this shield, on which is imprinted the lightning of Jupiter, that Vulcan shows Venus in our picture – though the episode itself does not appear in the *Aeneid*. To the right of the picture the Cyclops bring up Aeneas' plumed helmet and armored breastplate.

FIG. 1 Lempereur's engraving
The Forge of Vulcan

FIG. 2 Boucher, *Forge of Vulcan*, Louvre

Our picture differs from the final version in several details, notably in the absence of the two cupids – one resting on Venus' chariot, the other flying away with a bow and arrow – and in the treatment of the landscape – rocky and mountainous in the finished version, hidden by clouds in ours. Both of these pictures can be related to an overdoor Pierre painted for the *Salon de Compagnie* of the Hôtel de Rohan in 1751.[3] In this picture, one of a set of four painted for the Cardinal Armand de Soubise (1717–56), Venus is seated on a cloud and a cupid pushes his way between the goddess and Vulcan at the bottom of the picture. However, Vulcan's torso, firmly modelled and draped with a red cloak, is posed in a way similar to our picture, though there are differences in the angle at which he holds Aeneas' shield, and the composition of the overdoor is generally more static.[4] In our version, the draperies of both Venus and Vulcan, the latter's flowing hair and the upward motion of the Cyclops who hurry to give Aeneas' arms to their master, all help reinforce the dynamism of the tondo composition. Although Lempereur's engraving did not appear until 1762, it seems probable that the picture from which it was made, and also our version, were painted several years earlier, and should be dated to the late 1740's.

Pierre would certainly have known Boucher's famous painting of this subject [FIG. 2], painted in 1732 and in the collection of Claude-Henri Watelet, who owned, among others, Pierre's *Rape of Europa*.[5] But whereas

17 Jean-Baptiste-Marie Pierre, *The Forge of Vulcan*

FIG. 3 C. Natoire,
Fire,
Musée Rolin, Atun

Boucher's composition provided the inspiration for at least two paintings of the subject by Pierre's contemporaries – Natoire's *morceau de réception* of 1734 (Musée Fabre, Montpellier) and Carle Van Loo's *Venus Commissioning Arms for Aeneas*, painted the following year (Private collection, Paris), Pierre typically shows his independence from this slightly older generation of history painters in his treatment of this traditional theme. Although his overdoor was influenced by Boucher's painting, Pierre's *Forge of Vulcan* is closer to the work of another artist with whom he was associated in the 1740's and who was long thought to have been his teacher. Pierre may well have known Charles Natoire's second painting of this theme [FIG. 3], painted as part of a decorative series for the *fermier-général*, Pierre Grimod du Fort, in 1741 and engraved by Pierre Aveline. As its title suggests, Natoire's *Fire* (Musée Rolin, Autun) was one of a series of the four elements, and Pierre's *Forge of Vulcan* may also have been intended to fulfil a similarly decorative function.[6]

We know of at least one other sketch by Pierre of this theme, his *Venus at the Forge of Vulcan* (University of New Mexico Art Museum, Albuquerque), which has been dated to 1760, and treats the more usual moment of Venus requesting the arms in Vulcan's forge.[7] A painted copy after Lempereur's engraving is in the Bruckenthal Museum, Sibiu, Roumania, and this replica was itself engraved by Francesco del Pedro (1749–1806).[8]

Notes

[1] Y. Sjoberg, *Inventaire du Fonds Français, Graveurs du XVIIIe siècle*, Paris, 1977, vol. 14, pp. 289–90.

[2] *Virgil, the Aeneid*, trans. W. F. Jackson Knight, London, 1956, p. 214.

[3] Halbout, *op. cit.*, no. 54.

[4] I wish to acknowledge the generosity of M. Pariset, Conservateur du Musée de l'histoire de France, for granting me access to the Hôtel de Rohan.

[5] Ananoff, *op. cit.*, vol. 1, no. 85.

[6] *Charles-Joseph Natoire (1700–77), peintures, dessins, estampes et tapisseries des collections publiques françaises*, exhib. cat., Troyes, Nimes, Rome, 1977, no. 22, pp. 65–6.

[7] P. Walch, 'French eighteenth-century oil sketches from an English collection', *New Mexico Studies in the Fine Arts*, 5 (1980), p. 29.

[8] Th. von Frimmel, op. cit., p. 23; del Pedro's engraving is reproduced in the exhibition catalogue *Pitture, disegni e stampe del '700 dallo collezioni dei Musei Civici di Storia ed Arte di Trieste*, Museo Sartorio, Trieste, 1972, no. 178.

Jean-Baptiste-Marie Pierre

18 *The Rape of Europa*

Oil on canvas, H.96in. W.108½in.

Coll. Claude-Henri Watelet, *Catalogue de tableaux, dessins montés et en feuilles . . . le tout provenant du cabinet de feu M. Watelet*, Paris, 12 June 1786, no. 14, sold with Boucher's *Rape of Europa* and *Mercury Confiding the Infant Bacchus* as one lot to the dealer Saubert for 3,423 livres;[1] nineteenth-century provenance unknown; Private Collection, New York.

Lent by a Private Collector, New York.

Exhibition: Paris, Salon 1750, no. 56.

According to Alexandre Paillet, Pierre painted this *Rape of Europa* to complete the decoration of the salon of his friend, the celebrated *amateur*, collector and theoretician, Claude-Henri Watelet (1718–86), who owned over twenty works by the artist.[2] The *Rape of Europa* was exhibited in the Salon of 1750 and may have been intended, along with the other history paintings Pierre submitted that year (*Leda, Psyche, The Presentation at the Temple*) to counter allegations that he was wasting his talents in painting *bambochades*.[3] However, the picture was largely overlooked by salon critics in favor of the more obviously erotic *Leda* – 'tout le monde en a senti l'effet et il ne s'est point arrêté aux yeux' – although Pierre was praised for his facility, his vigorous coloring and his masterful draughtsmanship.[4] As the critic and collector Baillet de Saint-Julien pointed out, 'son pinceau est aisé, coulant et voluptueux', an apt description of Pierre's technique in this ambitious decorative painting.[5]

The story of Jupiter's abduction of Europa, the beautiful daughter of the King of Tyre, comes from Ovid's *Metamorphoses* (II/835–75), which Pierre would have known through the immensely popular translation of the abbé Banier (1737 and later editions). Pierre has followed Ovid quite closely in certain details: the muscular neck of the bull, his small, polished horns strewn with garlands, and his amiable and placid expression are distinctly indicated in the text. But Europa's fright and her anxious glance towards the shore behind her are understated in keeping with the decorative quality of the work. And while there are passages of virtuistic painting – above all in Europa's swirling draperies, the head and neck of the bull and the triton who feeds the animal with flowers – the ancillary figures are not depicted with the same flair and this large composition is somewhat static. Pierre's *Europa*, implied Baillet de Saint-Julien, is to be admired rather than adored.[6]

Pierre looked to Venetian examples of this celebrated myth. He would have seen Veronese's *Rape of Europa* in Venice – the picture was on display in the Doge's palace from 1733 and Pierre visited the city on his way back to Paris from Rome in 1740. He was even more familiar with a copy after Veronese (National Gallery, London), in the Orléans collection and then considered a *modello* for the *Rape of Europa*. Among the small group of pictures inventoried after his death we also find 'un tableau peint sur toile dans son cadre doré representant l'Enlevement d'Europe par Benedette Castiglione'.[7]

Pierre also drew inspiration from examples nearer home. His *Rape of Europa* was part of a decorative ensemble and was sold with Boucher's *Rape of Europa* [FIG. 1] and *Mercury Confiding the Infant Bacchus to the Nymphs* (Wallace Collection, London), dated some sixteen years earlier than our painting.[8] Pierre has followed Boucher in representing Jupiter in the form of an eagle hovering above Europa – a detail not found in Ovid – and in his portrayal of the three *amoretti* who watch over Europa with their garlands of flowers and love's bow and arrow. In fact, Pierre's *Rape of Europa* is a sequel to the moment represented by Boucher. The latter has

FIG. 1 Boucher, *Rape of Europa*, Wallace Collection, London

FIG. 2 Pierre, *Rape of Europa*, Metropolitan Museum, New York

FIG. 3 Pierre, *Allegory of Victory*, Chicago Art Institute

chosen to paint the scene in which Europa is encouraged by her maidens to mount the friendly bull. Pierre depicts the abduction itself where Europa's mood has changed from pastoral gaiety to tremulous fear.

Pierre would return to this theme seven years later in a tapestry cartoon for the Gobelins. He painted *The Rape of Europa* for the *Loves of the Gods* cycle commissioned for the Marquis de Marigny in 1757 (see entry 16). This picture, formerly in the Musée d'Arras, was destroyed during the first world war and is known today through a beautiful red chalk drawing at the Metropolitan Museum, New York [FIG. 2]. Here Pierre has portrayed the episode that Boucher painted for Watelet, and he has followed Boucher even more closely in the pyramidal grouping of Europa and her followers.[9]

The pose of the majestic figure of Europa in our picture recalls the fine *Allegory of Victory* at the Chicago Art Institute [FIG. 3]. This drawing, which may have been made at the time of the Peace of Aix-la-Chapelle (1748) has obvious stylistic affinities with the 1750 *Rape of Europa*, above all in the drawing of the seated Victory's right hand, the turn of her neck, the modelling of her breast and the folds of her drapery.[10] Pierre's picture was engraved by Louis-Simon Lempereur in 1762 and a print exhibited in the Salon of the following year. A copy of the *Rape of Europa*, done after this engraving, is in the Bruckenthal Museum, Sibiu, Roumania.[11]

Notes

[1] From the annotated sales catalogue in the Institut d'Art et d'Archéologie, Paris.

[2] A. Paillet, *Catalogue de tableaux, dessins montés et en feuilles . . . le tout provenant du cabinet de feu M. Watelet*, Paris, 12 June 1786, p. 7.

[3] The point is made in M. Halbout, *J. B. M. Pierre, Vie et oeuvre: Essai de catalogue des Peintures et des Dessins*, Mémoire dactylographie de l'Ecole du Louvre, 1970, pp. 56–64. I am most grateful to Mme Halbout for letting me consult her unpublished study of the artist.

[4] L. G. Baillet de Saint-Julien, *Lettres sur la Peinture à un Amateur*, Geneve, 1750, p. 20.

[5] *Ibid.*, p. 19.

[6] *Ibid.*, p. 19, 'l'enlèvement d'Europe n'a pas été moins loué que ce dernier : mais a peut-être attiré moins de regards'.

[7] A.N., *Minutier Central*, XXXI/253, *Inventaire après décès*, Jean-Baptiste-Marie Pierre, 'dans la bibliothèque'. The picture was presumably a copy, as it was given no separate valuation.

[8] A. Ananoff, *François Boucher*, 2 vols, Paris, 1976, vol. 1, nos. 104 and 105.

[9] The drawing appeared in *Vom Manierismus bis in die Goethezeit*, exhib. cat., Galerie Arnoldi-Livie, Munich, 1982, no. 33.

[10] See *Dessins français de l'Art Institute de Chicago de Watteau à Picasso*, Paris Louvre, 1976–7, no. 12.

[11] Th. von Frimmel, 'Bilder von J. B. M. Pierre in Hermannstadt und in Arras', *Blätter für Gemäldekunde*, 3 (1906), pp. 23–4, where this is incorrectly listed as Watelet's painting.

18 Jean-Baptiste-Marie Pierre, *The Rape of Europa* (This picture will not be shown in New York)

Jean-Baptiste-Marie Pierre

19 *The Judgment of Paris*

Oil on canvas, H.25in. W.31½in.

Coll. Dubois, *Catalogue des tableaux, gouaches, figures et bustes de
marbre . . . composant le cabinet de M. Dubois marchand joaillier à Paris*,
18 December 1788, no. 65, purchased by Carrier for 80 livres;[1] nineteenth-century provenance unknown; Private Collection, Switzerland;
Stair Sainty Matthiesen.

In 1755 Frederick the Great of Prussia commissioned four huge history
paintings for the decoration of the Marmorsaal (Marble Salon) in the
Neue Palais, Potsdam. The artists chosen were Antoine Pesne, Frederick's
Premier Peintre, who died before completing his *Abduction of Helen*, and
three of the leading history painters in France, Van Loo, Restout and
Pierre, who were to paint the *Sacrifice of Iphigenia*, the *Triumph of Bacchus*
and the *Judgment of Paris* [FIG. 1] respectively.[2] In the notes he assembled
for his obituary notice on Carle Van Loo, Dandré-Bardon recorded that
the artist agreed to have his painting finished by Easter 1757 and that he
received the sum of 12,000 livres for the *Iphigenia* in three instalments.
It is likely that the same conditions applied for Restout and Pierre.[3] In the
event, Van Loo and Restout both exhibited their Prussian commissions,
once the Seven Years' War had begun, at the Salon of 1757. But as Grimm
noted in the *Correspondance Littéraire*, Pierre's *Judgment of Paris*, though
expected, did not appear.[4] Pierre did not finish his *Judgment of Paris* until
the summer of 1759, when it could be seen in his studio: a detailed
description of the picture first appeared in the *Feuille Nécessaire* for 2 July
1759.[5] He then exhibited it, along with the *Beheading of John the Baptist*
(Musée Calvet, Avignon) and the *Descent from the Cross* (Versailles
Cathedral), in the Salon of 1761, where it received qualified praise from
most critics, except for Diderot, who detested the picture: 'Si le roi de
Prusse s'entend un peu en peinture, que fera-t-il de ce mauvais Jugement
de Paris?'.[6]

The problem with the final composition, as most critics were quick to point
out, was that the enormous size of the canvas (14 feet by 21 feet) could not
sustain a scene in which there were so few *dramatis personae*. Unlike Van
Loo's *Iphigenia* and Restout's *Bacchus* – 'tableaux qui étoient susceptibles
d'un grand nombre de figures' – the story of the momentous beauty contest
on Mount Gargarus, whose consequences would set in motion the epic
Trojan war, required a hushed and dramatic setting, 'une grande silence,

FIG. 1 Pierre, *Judgment of Paris*, Potsdam

19 Jean-Baptiste-Marie Pierre, *The Judgment of Paris*

une profonde solitude et la chute du jour'.[7] Diderot criticized Pierre for including both cupids and the Graces, figures who do not appear in Ovid's telling of the story – accessories which he imputed to Pierre's lack of imagination. Here he was less just than the author of a generally critical review which appeared in the *Observateur Littéraire*. The latter dismissed Paris as too rustic and complained that he was not dressed in Phrygian costume, but conceded that Pierre was faced with 'un trop vaste théâtre pour une scène peu nombreuse'.[8]

Such problems are not apparent in the preparatory sketch Pierre painted for the final picture – a bravura exercise in pinks, creams and blues which can be dated to the late 1750's. Paris has just handed the golden apple to Venus, who has won over the shepherd, not only by her great beauty, but by promising him Helen as his mistress. The Graces rush to clothe her: Paris had demanded that he judge the three goddesses unclothed. On the left we see Minerva about to depart, and above her, Juno leaving the scene in a chariot drawn by peacocks. The contrast between the fair-skinned attendants and the more ruddy shepherd, the handling of the tree in the background and the disposition of light bring to mind the *Bacchus and Ariadne* (Stanford University Museum of Art, Stanford, California), which is dated to around 1755.[9]

Pierre kept the central group practically intact in the final composition, although he replaced Paris's dramatic but inexplicable gesture in the sketch with the more conventional one of handing Venus the golden apple. The accessories are much changed, however. The landscape and grazing animals occupy a greater space, which inevitably diminishes the dramatic intensity of the moment of Paris's choice. The figure of Minerva, scowling behind her as she retrieves her garments, the figure of Jealousy beside her and the departing Juno above, create an imbalance in the composition and detract attention from the episode that occupies the center of the stage.

None of these difficulties appear in the preparatory sketch, where the play of light works to fix attention on the central group and where the figure of Minerva is balanced by the majestic oak on the right, thus giving greater symmetry and cohesiveness to the composition. Mariette may have written that Pierre's talents 'shone above all in large-scale works', but in this case it is the *première pensée* that represents a traditional theme more felicitously.

Pierre may have consciously attempted to introduce new elements in his interpretation of the *Judgment of Paris*. Diderot, who typically recreated the picture as he would have preferred it, has Paris seated on a rock, the light of the day about to fade, and the three goddesses still in the shepherd's presence – features beautifully depicted in Noël-Nicolas Coypel's painting of the subject of 1728 [FIG. 2], and taken up in Boucher's *Judgment of Paris* of 1754. Pierre, constrained in some measure by the horizontal format, has concentrated upon the amorous implications of Paris' choice, and in his assured grouping of cupids and graces shows himself a master of the gently erotic.

FIG. 2 N. N. Coypel, *Judgment of Paris*, Nationalmuseum, Stockholm

Notes

[1] The dimensions given in Dubois' sale catalogue are slightly smaller than those of our picture – H. 22 pouces, L. 27 pouces – but the description of the subject leaves no doubt: 'Venus, accompagnée des Graces, venant de recevoir la pomme des mains de Pâris'.

[2] Halbout, *op. cit.*, no. 76, gives a full discussion of the final version and the related commissions.

[3] *Bibl. Nat. Manuscrits*, Fonds Français, 13081, Dandré-Bardon *Recueil des Manuscrits divers*, fol. 279. This is not a receipt but a note made by Dandré-Bardon himself.

[4] F. M. Grimm, et al., *Correspondance Littéraire*, 16 vols, Paris, 1877–82, vol. 3, p. 427.

[5] *Feuille Nécessaire*, 2 July 1759, pp. 340–1.

[6] 'If the King of Prussia knows anything about painting, what on earth will he do with this poor Judgment of Paris', *Diderot, Essai sur la peinture, Salons de 1759, 1761, 1763*, Hermann, editeurs des sciences et des arts, Paris, 1984, p. 124.

[7] *Ibid.*, p. 126.

[8] 'Observations d'une Société d'amateurs sur les tableaux exposés au salon cette année, 1761', *L'Observateur Littéraire*, 1761, vol. 3, pp. 19–20.

[9] M. Halbout and P. Rosenberg, 'A propos de Jean-Baptise-Marie Pierre', *The Stanford Museum*, 4–5 (1975), p. 14.

Joseph-Marie Vien
Montpellier 1716–1809 Paris

Little is known of Vien's training before he arrived in Paris in 1740, where he entered the Academy Schools. Receiving the *Grand Prix* in 1743, he travelled to Rome the following year, where Jean-François De Troy was Director. His early style has a certain affinity with De Troy, but gradually he became more influenced by Batoni and also experimented with working from nature. Returning to Paris in 1750, Vien was received in 1754 with *Daedalus and Icarus* (Ecole des Beaux Arts, Paris) and quickly established an international reputation. He resisted the offers of the King of Denmark and Empress of Russia to take up appointments at their Courts and became a full Professor at the Academy in 1759. Encouraged by the Comte de Caylus, he was the first French artist to adopt the 'neo-Greek' style with his *Marchande d'amours* (or *Seller of Cupids*), now at Fontainebleau. In 1775 he was sent to Rome to replace Natoire, where he supervised the training of both David and Peyron, further encouraging the development of French Neo-classicism. After his return to France in 1781 his painting became less confident and more stylized, but he continued to paint even after his appointment as First Painter in 1789. He exhibited for the last time at the Salon of 1793 and was made a Count and Senator of the Empire by Napoleon shortly before his death. Thomas Gaehtgens' monographic study of the artist is forthcoming.

Joseph-Marie Vien

20 *Saint Theresa*

Oil on canvas, H.43½in. w.36in.
Signed, center left on cover of book: *Vien 175(5?)*.

Coll. Early provenance unknown; Stair Sainty Matthiesen.

FIG. 1 J-M. Vien, *Saint Theresa* (detail)

Although very little is known about the history or the provenance of this painting, it is documented by Vien himself in his autobiographical *Mémoires* published by Aubert in 1867. Recording a conversation with Caylus, which Vien dated to 1756, the antiquarian is supposed to have mentioned his excitement at seeing the *Saint Theresa* completed. Caylus had already seen the work in preparation, noted Vien, and had found the Saint's head, already finished, 'charming'.

> 'No doubt, my friend', says Caylus, 'she looks like that young Carmelite whose beauty you have praised so fulsomely – the one who was requested by the Mother Superior to don her ceremonial costume so that you could see how nuns dressed when they take part in the service'.[1]

From this it seems likely that Vien's picture was a commission from a Carmelite convent, and that, by its small size and intimist character, it was destined for private rather than public contemplation.

In any event, the richly impasted draperies, the absolutely assured handling – note the folds of the nun's cowl and the edge of the white cloth against her rosy cheeks – and the fine modelling of the nun's hands [FIG. 1] are of a purity rarely achieved in Vien's work. *Saint Theresa* recalls the monumental *Saint Martha* series, painted between 1746 and 1751 for the cloister of the Capuchin friars of Sainte-Marthe de Tarascon.[2] Yet by now Vien was able to reconcile his sources with far less effort than in the large-scale works. The pose of the Saint, which is entirely traditional and which Vien could have seen in countless religious paintings – but notably Guido Reni's influential *Vision of Saint Philip Neri* (Church of S. Maria in Vallicella, Rome) – nonetheless recalls Le Brun's *Saint Theresa* painted for the Carmelite convent in the Rue St Jacques and engraved by Mariette. The nun's habit, the outstretched hands, the upward-looking eyes are common to both paintings.

However, in its muted tonal range, its subdued and harmonious interplay of blacks, browns and creams which contrast with the cadmium tablecloth on the left, Vien's *Saint Theresa* bears comparison with the work of a very different sort of artist, the brilliant provençal painter, Pierre-Hubert Subleyras (1699–1749), whom Vien had met in Rome. It is noteworthy that among the pictures Vien owned, a sketch by Subleyras representing an *Apotheosis of a Saint* (Musée de Picardie, Amiens) has the central figure posed in supplication, hands outstretched, in a position that is reminiscent of Vien's *Saint Theresa*.[3]

Notes

[1] F. Aubert, 'Joseph-Marie Vien', *G.B.A.*, 23, 1867, p. 180.

[2] T. W. Gaehtgens, 'Joseph-Marie Vien et les peintures de la légende de Sainte-Marthe', *Revue de l'Art*, 23, 1974, pp. 64–9.

[3] *Ibid.*, p. 69, reproduced.

20 Joseph-Marie Vien, *Saint Theresa*

Joseph-Marie Vien

21 *Venus, Wounded by Diomedes, is Saved by Iris*

Oil on canvas, H.63¾in. w.81¾in.
Signed lower left: *jos. m. vien 1775*.

Coll. Comte Vincent Potocki; his sale (Paris?, 1781?), no. 253 (Lugt 3343); nineteenth-century provenance unknown; Versailles, Hôtel Rameau, 15 June 1977, no. 48, *Mars et Venus*; Heim Gallery, London, 1981; Private Collection, London; Stair Sainty Matthiesen.

Exhibitions: Paris, Salon 1775, no. 4; Toledo, Chicago, Ottawa, 1975–6, *The Age of Louis XV: French Painting 1710–74*, no. 114; London, Heim Summer exhibition, 1981, *Art as Decoration*, no. 12.

The story of Venus wounded by Diomedes forms the climax to Book 5 of Homer's *Iliad*. Diomedes, Minerva's champion, fells Aeneas with a stone and is on the point of killing him when Venus sweeps down and envelops her son in her robes, thus preventing his imminent death. Diomedes, furious, tracks down the goddess, insulting her and wounding her with his spear. At this point Venus lets Aeneas fall from her protective cover, but Apollo arrives on the scene in time to catch him and shroud him in a cloud, preventing for a second time the death of the Trojan hero. Venus, faint and in pain, is rescued by Iris who leads her away from the battle and brings her to Mars, who offers the goddess his chariot which will take her back to Olympus.

It is this last moment that Vien represented in his *Venus Wounded by Diomedes*, painted in 1775 and exhibited in the Salon of that year. This was the last secular work he would paint before leaving to take up the directorship of the French Academy in Rome, and the first of four Homeric pictures he would exhibit in the Salons of 1775 to 1783. If Diderot was fully aware of the pictorial difficulties presented by the successive stages of the encounter between Venus and Diomedes – 'Il y a là soixante vers à décourager l'homme le mieux appélé à la poésie' – Vien had less difficulty in choosing the appropriate moment from the epic.[1] For the artist followed, almost to the letter, the description of the scene given by his mentor, the Comte de Caylus, in his *Tableaux tirés de l'Iliade* – a recipe book of Greek and Roman subjects for the use of history painters published in 1757. Picture no. 6 from the fifth book of the Iliad was described by Caylus in considerable detail. Mars was to be shown hurrying to help Iris who assists Venus into the god's chariot – even though he has to be begged to give up his horses in the *Iliad*. The central group was to be surrounded by a protective cloud, its luminosity brought out by the contrast with Mars' black horses, which offered 'une magnifique opposition'. Finally, noted Caylus,

> To join together the two moments described in Homer, I would show Iris standing in the chariot, holding the horses' reins in one hand, while supporting Venus with the other, assisted by Mars, attentive as an anxious lover . . .'.[2]

As becomes evident, Vien has looked to Caylus rather than Homer in his interpretation of this theme. The main group is bathed in a blond light which places the gods outside the carnage depicted in the background. The darkness of Mars' horses do indeed contrast with Venus' pallor, the whiteness of her robe and the soft pinks and creams of Iris behind her. Vien also followed Caylus' suggestions for the emotional register of his composition. Iris looks down on Venus with almost maternal sollicitude and Mars hurries to catch her from swooning with all the earnest concern of 'un amant empressé'.[3]

Vien also seems to have taken to heart the spirit as well as the letter of Caylus' compendium, in his care to includes Venus' traditional attributes, the pair of white doves, which Caylus considered an essential adjunct, even

21 Joseph-Marie Vien, *Venus, Wounded by Diomedes, is Saved by Iris*

if their presence in this martial scene is misplaced. He was equally punctillious in representing the god's chariot with only two wheels – 'personne n'ignore que le genre de ces derniers n'avoit que deux roues' – and in dressing Venus in 'the lightest, most voluptuous and gently-colored garment . . . in which the goddess' girdle must not be forgotten'.[4] Vien's *Venus Wounded by Diomedes* corresponds, then, to Caylus' presumptuous claim to have provided artists with 'chaque sujet . . . pour ainsi dire, placé sur le chevalet'.[5] It is a mark of his influence over the last of the *Premier Peintres* that eighteen years after the publication of the *Tableaux tirés de l'Iliade*, and nine years after his death, Caylus' injunctions could still be translated into paint with such fidelity.

However, the critics who reviewed Vien's painting at the Salon of 1775 were less than wholehearted in their response, and no one identified the source of Vien's interpretation of Homer. Although there was general praise for the refined harmonies of the artist's palette and the successful grouping of the almost life-size figures – 'il y a de l'accord, de l'harmonie' (Diderot) – the figure of Mars met with universal criticism. He reminded Diderot of a Savoyard rather than the god of war, and, at best, could not be said to have 'l'air fort martial'.[6] Pidansart de Mairobert, the art critic of the *Mémoires Secrets*, summed up the general consensus:

> When an artist picks a subject from Homer, he must have the poet's genius and above all his passion ('sa chaleur'), especially when he depicts the god of war.[7]

Vien paid little attention to such criticism, however, He would use almost the same figure for the bellicose Hector in his *Hector Convincing Paris to Fight for his Homeland* (Musée National de Fontainebleau), shown at the Salon of 1779. Hector wears the same costume as Mars, and his pose is almost identical, but reversed.

For all this, *Venus Wounded by Diomedes*, with its cool pinks, greens and mauves, its erudite allusions and its strong erotic charge – 'le tableau de la beauté dont on voit couler le sang est toujours un object intéressant' as Caylus had remarked[8] – was Vien's most ambitious and heroic Grecian painting to date. His attraction to this little-exploited theme was furthermore prescient, and a later generations of 'pure classicists' – including David, Ingres, Gagneraux and Flaxman – would turn to this episode for its refined sensuality and charged opposition.[9]

Vien's painting must have entered the collection of the Polish noble, Comte Vincent Potocki (d. 1825), almost immediately. It was one of the few contemporary French paintings in the Grand Chamberlain's enormous collection of some 300 pictures, catalogued in Warsaw, but probably sold in Paris in 1781. Potocki's interest in the French school seems to have waned shortly thereafter – his collection had included some twenty works by or after Boucher and a generous and representative sample of French seventeenth- and eighteenth-century paintings from Poussin to Vernet.[10] In a second sale of his monumental print collection in 1820 there were very few French pictures in the catalogue, but it is worth noting that Potocki owned a *première pensée* for Vien's celebrated *Sleeping Hermit*, painted in 1753.[11]

Notes

[1] *Diderot Salons*, ed. Seznec and Adhémar, 4 vols, Oxford, 1957–67, vol. 1, p. 131.

[2] A-C-P. de Caylus, *Tableaux tirés de l'Iliade, de l'Odysée d'Homère et de l'Enéide de Virgile*, Paris, 1757, p. 39.

[3] *Ibid.*, p. 39.

[4] *Ibid.*, pp. xxxix, xl, lxxviii.

[5] *Ibid.*, p. v.

[6] *Diderot, op. cit.*, vol. 4, p. 276; *La Lanterne Magique aux Champs Elysées*, Paris, 1775, p. 11.

[7] L. Petit de Bachaumont, et al., *Mémoires Secrets*, 36 vols, London, 1777–89, vol. 13, p. 186.

[8] Caylus, *op. cit.*, p. 37.

[9] See the listing of specific works in *Art as Decoration*, Heim summer exhibition, London, 1981, no. 12.

[10] *Catalogue des dessins, tableaux, miniatures . . . contenus dans le cabinet de S.E. Mr le Comte Vincent Potocki*, Warsaw, 1780 (Lugt 3343).

[11] *Catalogue d'une collection nombreuse d'estampes anciennes et modernes . . . provenant du Cabinet de M. Le Comte V.P.*, Paris, 9–28 February 1820, no. 859.

INVENTORY
of Paintings by the Ten 'First Painters to the King'
in Public Collections in the United States

by Alan P. Wintermute B.A.

The Inventory which follows is an effort to record, as comprehensively as possible, the complete holdings of paintings by the ten 'First Painters' in United States museums, loosely following the format established by Pierre Rosenberg in his 1982 *France in the Golden Age* catalogue.

We have attempted to contact all American museums which might have holdings in seventeenth- and eighteenth-century French paintings and have collected photographs of all the paintings attributed to the 'First Painters' from the institutions which responded to our inquiries. Of course, any such list is inevitably incomplete and no doubt the attributions of certain pictures will change and others be debated. We welcome such discussion and only hope that this exhibition and catalogue will encourage in scholars, curators and the public renewed interest in the study of the artists here represented.

The following are a few explanatory notes which may help the reader in consulting the Inventory:

Artists have been listed alphabetically, and their works listed alphabetically by institution.

Museums have been identified only by city, except in cases where they are affiliated with another institution such as a university, and where a city has more than one major collection of old master paintings.

Beside the title of each painting we have listed the date (recorded or presumed) of its execution and its dimensions in inches, when these have been available.

We have listed a single bibliographic reference for each painting when we have located one both recent and informative. In many cases where no reference has been cited the catalogue or handbook of the museum owning the picture will aid further research. The references cited are all included in the Bibliography at the end of this Inventory.

The number which follows the name of a reference refers to a catalogue number, unless it is preceded by 'p.', referring then to a page number.

Listings with asterisks (*) beside them indicate that their attributions, while accepted here, are questioned by certain scholars. Remarks within parentheses beside references, such as 'Ananoff, 533 (studio)', reflect that author's opinion.

A photographic reproduction accompanies each painting published as autograph, or autograph with workshop collaboration. Those published as questionable attributions have been separately alphabetized by artist and institution and listed following the accepted works, unaccompanied by reproductions.

Generally, we have tended to be generous in accepting the attribution a museum has given its picture when there has seemed at least a real possibility that it is correct. For several of these artists – Pierre being perhaps the most notable example – so little research has been published that defining the parameters of their *oeuvres* lies beyond the aspirations of this Inventory.

One caveat: Although during the year in which this catalogue has been in preparation we have had an opportunity to see many of the works listed, the majority we have studied only through photographs, and so have relied for our attributions largely on scholarly consensus. In instances in which we have ourselves examined the paintings, or in which scholarly opinion was unavailable or divided, we have relied on our own judgment.

The responsibility for all attributions finally rests with us, but the Inventory could not have been assembled without the advice and help of many scholars, especially museums' curators, who generously offered of their time and knowledge, and all of whom, although far too numerous to name, we most sincerely thank.

François Boucher

Albuquerque, NM (UNM)

1 *Boreas and Orythia* 1747
$11\frac{3}{4} \times 9\frac{1}{4}$ (Sketch)
Ananoff.349

2 *Putti*
$14 \times 17\frac{1}{3}$ (Sketch)

3 *Monument to Mignard* 1743
$28 \times 22\frac{1}{2}$ (Sketch)
Marandel.3

1

2

3

Baltimore, MD (Walters)

4 *Idyllic Scene: Fisherman w/Young Woman*
1769
$25\frac{5}{8} \times 21\frac{5}{8}$
Ananoff.666

5 *Idyllic Scene: Pastoral Repast* 1769
$25\frac{1}{4} \times 21\frac{1}{4}$
Ananoff.667

4

5

Boston, MA (MFA)

6 *Portrait of a Woman* 1734
$22\frac{1}{3} \times 18\frac{1}{5}$
Ananoff.109

7 *Shepherd Boy Playing Bagpipes*
$21\frac{3}{4} \times 19\frac{5}{8}$

8 *Returning from the Market* 1769
$81\frac{1}{4} \times 113$
Ananoff.661

9 *Halt at the Spring* 1765
$82\frac{1}{2} \times 108\frac{1}{4}$
Ananoff.660

6

7

8

9

Boston, MA (Gardner)

10 *The Car of Venus* 1750
$34\frac{3}{4} \times 27\frac{1}{2}$
Ananoff.356

10

Cambridge, MA (Fogg)

11 *Marquise de Pompadour* 1758
$32 \times 25\frac{1}{2}$
Ananoff. 497

11

Champaign, IL (Krannert)

12 *Les Vendanges* 1756
$65 \times 46\frac{1}{2}$
Ananoff. 325

12

Chicago, IL

13 *Pensent – ils au Raisins?* 1747
$31\frac{4}{5} \times 27$
Ananoff. 310

13

Cincinnati, OH

14 *The Water Mill* 1764
24×32
Ananoff. 587

15 *The Washerwoman* 1764
$25 \times 32\frac{1}{2}$
Ananoff. 586

14

15

Cleveland, OH

16 *Cupids in Conspiracy* 1740
$27\frac{1}{5} \times 48\frac{1}{2}$
Ananoff. '80. 194

17 *Music and Dance* 1740
$27 \times 48 \cdot 7$
Ananoff. '80. 195

18 *Fountain of Venus* 1756
$92 \times 84\frac{1}{2}$

16

17

18

Columbia, SC

19 *Joseph and Jacob before the Pharoah* 1723
$22\frac{3}{4} \times 28\frac{5}{8}$
Ananoff. 9

19

Columbus, OH

20 *Earth: Vertumnus & Pomona* 1749
$34\frac{1}{5} \times 53\frac{5}{8}$
Ananoff. 329

20

Detroit, MI

21 *Birth of Venus* 1765
$69 \times 30\frac{1}{4}$
Ananoff.619

22 *Young Girl and Eros* 1750
$27\frac{3}{4} \times 22\frac{1}{2}$

21

22

Fort Worth, TX (Kimbell)

23 *The Sacrifice of Noah* 1727
$12\frac{3}{4} \times 25\frac{1}{2}$
Ananoff.31 (as lost)

24 *Noah Entering the Ark* 1727
$12\frac{3}{4} \times 25\frac{1}{2}$
Ananoff.30 (as lost)

25 *Juno Inducing Aeolus to Loose the Storm on Aeneas* 1769
$109\frac{1}{2} \times 79\frac{3}{4}$
Ananoff.674

26 *Venus Securing Arms of Vulcan for Aeneas* 1769
$87\frac{1}{2} \times 80\frac{5}{8}$
Ananoff.675

27 *The Birth of Bacchus* 1769
$87\frac{1}{2} \times 79\frac{1}{3}$
Ananoff.676

28 *Boreas Abducting Oreithyia* 1769
$107\frac{5}{8} \times 80\frac{5}{8}$
Ananoff.677

23

24

25

26

27

28

Hartford, CT (Wadsworth Atheneum)

29 *The Egg Seller* 1734
$42\frac{1}{4} \times 32\frac{3}{4}$
Ananoff.90

29

Houston, TX

30 *Les Pecheurs* 1744
37×31
Ananoff.274

30

Indianapolis, IN

31 *Idyllic Landscape w/Woman Fishing* 1761
18 × 26
Zafran.65

31

Kansas City, MO (Nelson Atkins)

32 *Diana and Callisto* 1759
22 × 27
Ananoff.518

33 *Landscape of Environs of Beauvais* 1740
49¾ × 63
Ananoff.175

32

33

Los Angeles, CA

34 *Les Confidences Pastorales* 1745
37 × 52
Ananoff.280

35 *Venus and Mercury Instructing Cupid* 1738
39⅜ × 51⅝
Ananoff.151

36 *Cupid Wounding Psyche* 1741
39⅜ × 51⅝
Ananoff.152

34

35

36

Louisville, KY (J. B. Speed)

37 *La Fontaine* 1730
21¼ × 25⅝
Ananoff.46

37

Malibu, CA (Getty)

38 *Fountain of Love* 1748
116 × 132¾
Ananoff.321

39 *The Bird Catchers* 1748
116 × 132¾
Ananoff.324

40 *Venus and Endymion* 1769
104½ × 34
Ananoff.670

41 *Venus on the Waves* 1769
104½ × 34
Ananoff.671

41a *The Letter*
49½ × 35 (Sketch)

41b *Two Shepherdesses*
49½ × 35 (Sketch)

38

39

40   41

41a

41b

Minneapolis, MN

42 *St John the Baptist* 1750
$64\frac{1}{2} \times 45\frac{1}{2}$
Ananoff. 361

42

New Orleans

43 *Woman with a Cat* 1730
$32 \times 25\frac{3}{4}$
Caraco. 85

43

New York (Frick)

* 44 *Allegory of Drawing* 1760
$15\frac{3}{4} \times 13$

* 45 *Allegory of Poetry* 1760
$15\frac{3}{4} \times 13$

46 *Mme Boucher* 1743
$22\frac{1}{2} \times 27$
Ananoff. 263

47 *Astronomy/Hydraulics* 1751
$85\frac{1}{2} \times 38$
Ananoff. 371

48 *Comedy and Tragedy* 1751
$85\frac{1}{2} \times 30\frac{1}{2}$
Ananoff. 366

49 *Poetry and Music* 1751
$85\frac{1}{2} \times 38$
Ananoff. 370

50 *Architecture/Chemistry* 1751
$85\frac{1}{2} \times 30\frac{1}{2}$
Ananoff. 365

51 *Fishing and Hunting* 1751
$85\frac{1}{2} \times 38$
Ananoff. 372

52 *Fowling and Horticult.* 1751
$85\frac{1}{2} \times 38$
Ananoff. 369

53 *Painting and Sculpture* 1751
$85\frac{1}{2} \times 30\frac{1}{2}$
Ananoff. 368

54 *Singing and Dancing* 1751
$85\frac{1}{2} \times 30\frac{1}{2}$
Ananoff. 367

55 *Spring* 1755
$22\frac{1}{2} \times 28\frac{3}{4}$
Ananoff. 454

56 *Summer* 1755
$22\frac{1}{2} \times 28\frac{3}{4}$
Ananoff. 455

57 *Autumn* 1755
$22\frac{1}{2} \times 28\frac{3}{4}$
Ananoff. 456

58 *Winter* 1755
$22\frac{1}{2} \times 28\frac{3}{4}$
Ananoff. 457

*59 *Girl with Roses* 1754
$21\frac{1}{2} \times 16\frac{3}{4}$
Ananoff. 435

44

45

46

47

48

49

50

51

52

58

60

59

53   54

61

55

56

New York (Met)

60 *Washerwomen* 1768
$94\frac{1}{2} \times 92\frac{1}{2}$
Ananoff. 655

61 *Shepherd's Idyll* 1768
$94\frac{1}{2} \times 92\frac{1}{2}$
Ananoff. 654

62 *Toilet of Venus* 1751
$42\frac{1}{2} \times 33\frac{1}{2}$
Ananoff. 376

63 *Interrupted Sleep* 1750
$29\frac{1}{2} \times 25\frac{1}{2}$
Ananoff. 363

64 *Monument Study* 1763
$15 \times 12\frac{1}{2}$ (Sketch)
Ananoff. 571

65 *Jupiter (as Callisto) and Diana* 1763
$25\frac{1}{2} \times 21\frac{3}{4}$
Ananoff. 576

66 *Angelica & Medoro* 1763
$25\frac{1}{2} \times 21\frac{3}{4}$
Ananoff. 575

67 *Campo Vaccino* 1734
$24\frac{1}{4} \times 30\frac{1}{2}$
Ananoff. 101

68 *Le Depart du Courrier* 1765
$12\frac{3}{4} \times 10\frac{1}{2}$
Ananoff. 594

69 *Project pour Diplôme* 1765
$15\frac{1}{2} \times 10\frac{1}{2}$ (Sketch)
Ananoff. 614

70 *Virgin and Child* 1765
$15\frac{3}{4} \times 13$
Zafran. 10

* **71** *Allegory of Lyric Poetry* 1753
$44\frac{3}{4} \times 63\frac{3}{4}$
(Studio collaboration)

* **72** *Allegory of Autumn* 1753
$45\frac{1}{4} \times 62\frac{3}{4}$
(Studio collaboration)

57

62

63

64

65

70

66

71

Notre Dame, IN (Snite)

73 *Offering of a Rose* 1765
36 × 28
Ananoff. 602

73

67

72

Pasadena, CA (Norton Simon)

*74 *Vertumnus and Pomona* 1745
$62\frac{3}{4} \times 66\frac{1}{3}$

75 *La Belle Villageoise* 1732
$16\frac{1}{8} \times 12\frac{5}{8}$
Ananoff. 78

74

68

Norfolk, VA (Chrysler)

72a *The Vegetable Vendor* 1732
95 × 67
Ananoff. 83

72a

75

69

Philadelphia, PA

76 *Jeune Femme Attachant Lettre au Col d'un Pigeon* 1770
28 × 22
Ananoff.688

76

Phoenix, AZ

77 *La Leçon de la Lecture* 1768
16 × 14
Slatkin.p.XIX

77

Pittsburgh, PA (Frick)

78 *L'Heureux Pecheur* 1732
95 × 67
Ananoff.82

78

Portland, OR

79 *Mme. de Pompadour* 1749
$29\frac{3}{8} \times 24\frac{1}{8}$
Zafran.28

79

Princeton, NJ

80 *Arion on the Dolphin* 1749
$33\frac{3}{4} \times 53\frac{3}{8}$
Ananoff.328

80

Providence, RI (RISD)

81 *L'Amour Oiseleur (L'Eté)* 1734
$28 \times 28\frac{3}{8}$
Ananoff.61

81

Raleigh, NC

82 *Allegory of Music* 1752
$26\frac{1}{2} \times 30$
Ananoff.432

*83 *Jupiter & Callisto* 1766
56 × 45
Ananoff.533 (3) (studio)

84 *Venus Rising from the Waves* 1766
56 × 45
Ananoff.637 (studio collaboration)

85 *Landscape w/Castle and Mill* 1765
$20\frac{7}{8} \times 30\frac{3}{16}$
Ananoff.609

82

83

84

85

Rochester, NY (Memorial)

*86 *Venus and Cupid* 1725
$15 \times 12\frac{1}{2}$
Ananoff. 11(1) (as lost)

86

St Louis (City), MO

87 *Le Vieux Colombier* 1758
$27\frac{3}{16} \times 17\frac{7}{8}$
Ananoff. 513

87

San Diego, CA (Timkin)

88 *Lovers in the Park* 1758
$91\frac{1}{2} \times 76\frac{3}{4}$
Ananoff. 501

88

San Francisco, CA

89 *Vertumnus and Pomona* 1757
$123\frac{3}{4} \times 72\frac{1}{2}$
Ananoff. 385

90 *Companions of Diana* 1745
$46\frac{1}{8} \times 36\frac{1}{8}$
Ananoff. 290

91 *Bacchantes* 1745
$46\frac{3}{16} \times 38\frac{1}{8}$
Ananoff. 288

92 *Virgin and Child* 1769
$17 \times 13\frac{3}{4}$
Ananoff. 662

89

90

91

92

San Marino, CA (Huntington)

93 *Venus and Cupid* 1769
$27\frac{1}{2} \times 22\frac{1}{2}$
Ananoff. 678

93

Springfield, MA

94 *Journey to Market* 1730
$16\frac{1}{8} \times 12\frac{1}{2}$
Ananoff. 53

94

Toledo, OH

95 *Mill at Charenton* 1758
$44\frac{1}{2} \times 57\frac{1}{2}$
Ananoff. 505

96 *The Footbridge* 1760
$19\frac{7}{8} \times 24$
Ananoff. 531

95

96

Washington, DC (Corcoran)

97 *La Musique* 1742
$41\frac{4}{5} \times 55\frac{1}{2}$

98 *The Bird Catchers* 1744
$34\frac{1}{3} \times 38$
Ananoff. 273

97

98

Washington, DC (Nat. Gallery)

99 *The Love Letter* 1750
$32 \times 29\frac{1}{2}$
Ananoff. 364

100 *Mme Bergeret* 1746
$56\frac{1}{4} \times 41$
Ananoff. 301

101 *Allegory of Music* 1764
$40\frac{3}{4} \times 51\frac{1}{5}$
Ananoff. 580

102 *Allegory of Painting* 1765
$40\frac{3}{4} \times 51\frac{1}{5}$
Ananoff. 581

103 *Venus Consoling Love* 1751
$42 \times 33\frac{1}{2}$
Ananoff. 377

99

100

101

102

103

Williamstown, MA (Clark Institute)

104 *Vulcan Presenting Arms to Venus for Aeneas* 1756
$16\frac{1}{4} \times 17$
Ananoff. 479

104

Worcester, MA

105 *Venus Rescuing Paris from Menelaus* 1765
$18\frac{1}{5} \times 22\frac{1}{2}$ (Sketch)
Ananoff. 613

105

QUESTIONABLE

Baltimore, MD (Museum)

La Colombe
$9\frac{1}{2} \times 7\frac{1}{2}$

Los Angeles, CA

Le Messager Fidele 1750
$38 \times 59\frac{1}{2}$
Ananoff. 364 (copy 15)

Phoenix, AZ

Two Amorini 1760
$23\frac{3}{4} \times 20$

Raleigh, NC

Abduction of Europa 1747
$63 \times 76\frac{1}{2}$
Ananoff. 350 (copy)

San Francisco CA

Music 1756
$38\frac{1}{8} \times 48$
Ananoff. 470(1) (copy)

Pensent – ils au Raisin? 1747
$30 \times 35\frac{1}{2}$
Ananoff. 309(6) (copy)

Washington, DC (Nat. Gallery)

Diana and Endymion 1765
$37\frac{1}{3} \times 54$
(Early Fragonard?)

Louis de Boullongne

Greenville, SC (Bob Jones)

106 *The Visitation* 1688
$122\frac{1}{2} \times 84\frac{1}{8}$
Schnapper, 1974, p.18

106

Notre Dame, IN (Snite)

107 *St Augustin Preaching at the Hippone in front of Bishop Valere* 1705
$27\frac{1}{4} \times 18\frac{1}{2}$

107

Providence, RI (RISD)

108 *Augustus orders closing Temple of Janus* study 1681
$28\frac{1}{2} \times 23$ (Sketch)

108

Antoine Coypel

Oberlin, OH

109 *The Finding of Moses* 1699
$44\frac{7}{8} \times 57\frac{1}{2}$
Schnapper, 1979, pp.59–67

109

Ponce, PR

110 *God Reproving Adam and Eve* 1704 (?)
$45\frac{3}{4} \times 35\frac{1}{4}$
Rosenberg, 1975, p.19

110

QUESTIONABLE

Lawrence, KA (H. F. Spencer)

The Rape of Europa
$15\frac{1}{2} \times 21\frac{1}{2}$

Charles Coypel

Louisville, KY (J. B. Speed)

111 *Education of the Virgin*
$36\frac{1}{4} \times 29$

111

Norfolk, VA (Chrysler)

111a *Thalie Chassée par la Peinture* 1732
26×32

111a

QUESTIONABLE

Columbia, SC

Venus, Tritons & Nymphs
$39 \times 49\frac{3}{4}$ (Italian eighteenth century)

Charles Le Brun

Detroit, MI

112 *Purification of the Virgin* 1645
$105\frac{3}{4} \times 77\frac{1}{4}$
Chomer.pp.183–9

112

Malibu, CA (Getty)

113 *The Crucifixion of St Andrew* 1647
$42 \times 39\frac{1}{2}$
Thuillier.10

113

Minneapolis, MN

114 *The Holy Family in Egypt* 1655–6
$20\frac{3}{8} \times 16\frac{5}{8}$

114

Ponce, PR

115 *Minerva & Venus Clipping Cupid's Wings*
1655–8
$45\frac{3}{4} \times 40\frac{1}{3}$
Rosenberg, 1982, p.41

115

QUESTIONABLE

Greenville, SC (Bob Jones)

Pentecost
$42\frac{5}{8} \times 29$
(Studio?)

Houston, TX (Menil Foundation Coll.)

Holy Family
(Studio?)

François Le Moyne

Albuquerque, NM (UNM)

*116 *Hercules and Cacus* 1710
$19\frac{1}{2} \times 23\frac{3}{4}$ (Sketch)
Marandel.59

*117 *Sacrifice of Iphegenia* 1720–5
$20\frac{1}{2} \times 24\frac{1}{4}$ (Sketch)
Marandel.58

116

117

Cambridge, MA (Fogg)

118 *Putti w/Accoutrements of Mars* 1721–4
$5\frac{1}{4} \times 4\frac{1}{4}$ (Sketch)
Bordeaux.40

118

Detroit, MI

119 *Cleopatra* 1724
$39\frac{1}{4} \times 32$
Bordeaux.45

119

Minneapolis, MA

*120 *Cleopatra* 1724
$40\frac{1}{2} \times 29\frac{1}{4}$
Bordeaux.45

121 *Vestal Virgin* 1724
$35 \times 42\frac{1}{5}$
Bordeaux.70

120

121

QUESTIONABLE

Albuquerque, NM (UNM)

Immaculata with David and Isaiah
$23\frac{1}{2} \times 11\frac{3}{4}$

Rochester, NY (Memorial)

Charity: Louis XV Bestowing Peace on Europe – (Sketch) 1729
$25 \times 31\frac{1}{2}$
Bordeaux.78 (copy)

Carle Van Loo

Albuquerque, NM (UNM)

122 *Putti* 1732
$8\frac{1}{4} \times 6$ (Sketch)
Marandel.85

***123** *St Elizabeth of Hungary*
$11 \times 8\frac{4}{5}$ (Sketch)

***124** *Satyr*
$6 \times 4\frac{1}{2}$ (Sketch)

125 *Three Graces* 1763–5
$23 \times 18\frac{1}{4}$ (Sketch)
Marandel.84

***126** *Darius*
$25\frac{3}{4} \times 36\frac{1}{2}$ (Sketch)

127 *Theseus Taming the Bull of Marathon* 1746
$25\frac{3}{4} \times 57\frac{1}{2}$ (Sketch)
Marandel.83

122

123

124

125

126

127

128

Cambridge, MA (Fogg)

***129** *La Camargo Enfant*
$34\frac{3}{4} \times 28\frac{1}{2}$

129

Detroit, MI

130 *Marriage of the Virgin* 1730
$23\frac{1}{4} \times 15\frac{3}{4}$
Sahut.9

130

Hartford, CT
(Wadsworth Atheneum)

131 *The Offering to Love* 1761
$63\frac{1}{5} \times 30\frac{7}{8}$

131

Los Angeles, CA

132 *Adoration of the Magi* 1760
$51 \times 41\frac{1}{2}$
Sahut. 196a (as lost)

133 *The Presentation of Christ*
$21\frac{3}{4} \times 15$ (Sketch)

132

133

New Orleans, LA

134 *Noli Me Tangere* 1735
$25\frac{1}{2} \times 19\frac{1}{4}$
Caraco. '83

134

Pittsburg, PA (Frick)

135 *Les Arts Suppliants* 1764
$30\frac{1}{4} \times 26\frac{1}{8}$
Sahut. 178

135

Princeton, NJ

136 *Rinaldo and Armida* 1743
$16\frac{1}{2} \times 19\frac{1}{4}$
Sahut. 90

136

Richmond, VA

137 *A Pasha Having His Mistress' Portrait
Painted* 1737
26×30
Sahut. 53

137

San Francisco, CA

138 *Sculpture* 1752–3
33×34
Sahut. 126

139 *Architecture* 1752–3
33×34
Sahut. 127

140 *Music* 1752–3
33×34
Sahut. 128

141 *Painting* 1752–3
33×34
Sahut. 125

138

139

140

141

QUESTIONABLE

Albuquerque, NM (UNM)
Flight into Egypt
$14\frac{1}{2} \times 10\frac{1}{2}$ (Sketch)

Baltimore, MD (Museum)
Mlle de Vollardeau
14×12

New York, (Met)
Woman on a Couch
21×27

Norfolk, VA (Chrysler)
Countess Deaurepare 1766
$57\frac{3}{4} \times 44\frac{1}{2}$

Saginaw, MI
Portrait of a Court Lady
51×38

Pierre Mignard

Honolulu, HI
*142 *Portrait of Three Children* 1647
$35 \times 46\frac{3}{4}$
Rosenberg, 1982, p. 69

142

Louisville, KY (J.B. Speed)
143 *Portrait of a Marshall of France* 1675
$56\frac{1}{2} \times 40\frac{1}{4}$
Nikolenko. 14

143

Raleigh, NC
144 *Christ and the Woman of Samaria* 1681
48×63
Rosenberg. 70

144

QUESTIONABLE

Columbus, OH
Louis XIV in Armor 1674
$25\frac{1}{4} \times 19\frac{1}{4}$
Queen Marie Therese
$52\frac{1}{2} \times 38\frac{3}{4}$

Greenville, SC (Bob Jones)
Head of Christ
$15\frac{1}{2} \times 13$

Hickory, NC
Comtesse de Champigny

Lexington, KY
Portrait of a Gentleman
$27\frac{1}{4} \times 20\frac{1}{2}$

New London, CT (Lyman Allen)
Portrait of a Lady
41×32
(Studio?)

New Orleans, LA (Gallier House)
Portrait of Louis XIV held in a Medallion by an Allegorical Figure Symbolizing Glory

Norfolk, VA (Chrysler)
Madonna and Child
$45 \times 37\frac{1}{2}$
(Studio)

Philadelphia, PA
Duchess of Chevreuse

Portland, OR
Portrait of the Sculptor Antoine Coysevox
$26\frac{1}{4} \times 22\frac{1}{4}$
(Circle, Studio?)

Jean Baptiste Marie Pierre

Albuquerque, NM (UNM)
145 *Vulcan's Forge* 1760
$9\frac{1}{2} \times 13$ (Sketch)
146 *Scene from Ancient History* 1755–60
$11\frac{1}{4} \times 9\frac{1}{2}$ (Sketch)
Marandel. 70

145

146

Amherst, MA (Mead)

*147 *Allegory of Sculpture* 1755
$35\frac{1}{2} \times 28\frac{1}{4}$
Zafran. 17

147

Dayton, OH

*148 *Temptation of Eve* 1745
$19 \times 22\frac{1}{2}$
Vasseur. pp. 2–5

148

Detroit, MI

149 *Adoration of the Shepherds* 1745
$110 \times 139\frac{3}{4}$
Halbout. pp. 169–76

149

New York (Met)

150 *Death of Harmonia*
$77\frac{1}{2} \times 58\frac{1}{4}$

150

San Francisco, CA

*151 *The Tale of the Cooper's Wife* 1750
$28\frac{3}{4} \times 22\frac{1}{2}$
Bordeaux. 17

151

Stanford, CA

152 *Bacchus and Ariadne* 1755
$31\frac{1}{4} \times 25\frac{1}{2}$
Zafran. 16

152

Joseph-Marie Vien

Albuquerque, NM (UNM)

153 *Political Allegory*
$15\frac{1}{2} \times 8$ (Sketch)
Marandel. 87

154 *Aeneas Arrives in Carthage and Meets Dido*
$12 \times 27\frac{1}{2}$ (Sketch)
Marandel. 86

153

154

Ponce, PR

155 *Greek Lady at the Bath* 1767
35×30
Zafran. 12

155

QUESTIONABLE

Albuquerque, NM (UNM)

Mucius Scaevola before Porsenna
$15\frac{1}{2} \times 19\frac{3}{4}$ (Sketch)

Selected Bibliography
of Inventory References

Ananoff, Alexandre	*Francois Boucher*, 2 vols, Lausanne–Paris, 1976.
Ananoff, Alexandre	*L'opera completa di Boucher*, Milan, 1980.
Bordeaux, Jean-Luc	*Francois Le Moyne and his generation*, Neuilly-sur-Seine, 1984.
Caraco, Edward P.	'New Acquisitions: Paintings by Eighteenth-Century French Masters', *Arts Quarterly*, October–December 1983.
Caraco, Edward P.	'New Acquisition: Francois Boucher's *Woman with a Cat*, Delightful Lesson on the Dangers of Love', *Arts Quarterly*, April–June 1985.
Chomer, M.	'The Purification of the Virgin', *Detroit Institute of Arts Bulletin*, vol. 55, no. 4, 1977.
Conisbee, Philip	*Painting in Eighteenth-Century France*, Oxford, 1981.
Halbout, Monique	'The Adoration of the Shepherds', *Detroit Institute of Arts Bulletin*, vol. 56, 1978.
Marandel, J. Patrice	*French Oil Sketches from an English Collection*, Houston, 1973–5.
Nikolenko, Lada	*Pierre Mignard, the Portrait Painter of the Grand Siècle*, Munich, 1983.
Rosenberg, Pierre	*The Age of Louis XV, French Painting 1710–74*, Toledo, Chicago, Ottawa, 1975.
Rosenberg, Pierre	*France in the Golden Age: Seventeenth-Century Painting in American Collections*, Paris, New York, Chicago, 1982.
Sahut, Marie-Catherine and Pierre Rosenberg	*Carle Van Loo 1705–65*, Nice, Clermont-Ferrand, Nancy, 1977.
Schnapper, Antoine	*Jean Jouvenet et la peinture d'histoire à Paris*, Paris, 1974.
Schnapper, Antoine	'The Moses of Antoine Coypel', *Allen Memorial Art Museum Bulletin*, vol. 37, no. 2, 1979–80.
Slatkin, Regina Shoolman	*François Boucher in North American Collections: 100 Drawings*, Washington, Chicago, 1973.
Thuillier, Jacques and Jennifer Montagu	*Charles Le Brun 1619–90*, Chateau de Versailles, 1963.
Vasseur, Dominique	'The Temptation of Eve: A New Attribution to Jean-Baptiste-Marie Pierre', *The Dayton Art Institute Bulletin*, vol. 39, December 1984.
Zafran, Eric M.	*The Rococo Age*, Atlanta, 1983.

Photo credits